STRELTSOV

A NOVEL

First published by Blizzard Media Ltd in 2021

Blizzard Books
Bedser Stand
Kia Oval
London
SE11 5SS

Typeset in Garamond
Design by Rob Whitehouse

This book is printed on paper certified by the Forest Stewardship Council®

First published 2021
© 2021 Jonathan Wilson
ISBN 978-1-915237-04-0
A CIP catalogue record for is available from the British Library

Printed by Micropress Printers Ltd

About the Author

Jonathan Wilson writes for the *Guardian* and *Sports Illustrated*. He is the author of eleven books of football history, including *Inverting the Pyramid*, *Angels With Dirty Faces* and *The Names Heard Long Ago*. *Streltsov* is his first novel.

Acknowledgements

This is a novel based on a true story and so required detailed research. It couldn't have been written without the help of Igor Volkov. I thank him profoundly, and must also express my gratitude to Sasha Goryunov, Vladimir Soldatkin, Axel Vartanyan, Igor Rabiner and Sergey Bondarenko.

Enormous thanks are due to Richard Beard for his thorough and sensitive edit. I'm grateful also to Jon Hotten and Tony McGowan for their thoughts on how to improve the text.

Thanks also to Matt Thacker and everybody at Trinorth for agreeing to publish the novel and all their work putting it together.

Глава первая

1996

TORPEDO-LUZHNIKI

Russian League: *P34 W10 D11 L13 F42 A51 Pts41.* **Final position:** *12th of 18.*
Russian Cup: *Lost in fifth round to Metallurg Lipetsk.*

You will, I hope, forgive my limitations.

I'd had a vodka too many the night before – how could you not on the anniversary? – but I wanted to get there before the worst of the heat. The weather had been stifling that week. Real Moscow in July heat. Sticky, humid, so your shirt clung to you from dawn till dusk and beyond. That's why I left early. I took the Metro to Ulitsa 1905 goda – much nearer Dinamo and CSKA than Torpedo, but then cemeteries aren't built for football teams – and bought a small bouquet from the kiosk on the corner.

By the time I'd walked to the gates of Vagankovo, cursing the suit I'd decided to wear, it was perhaps 6.30am, a slight mist still in the air. I walked down between the ashes, feeling the prickles of sweat begin to rise, sensing the alcohol on my skin. I probably shouldn't have worn a suit, but you do, don't you, to visit a cemetery? Or people of my generation do. The suit was too big for me now. Well, it had never really fit, but it had grown old and shapeless. I'd also grown old and shapeless, but where I'd got smaller, it had got bigger. We were like a disappointing marriage, growing further apart by the day.

It was a familiar route and I wasn't paying much attention. I'd come to the cemetery for many reasons over the years, personal and professional, but since 1970 I always went to one grave first. It was important to pay your respects. I laid the bouquet by the simple headstone, stepped back and bowed my head. I'd never worked out what you were supposed to do at gravesides, but some sort of gesture seemed important. The familiar sadness swelled in my throat. I wished I'd given her flowers while she was still alive. I blinked and turned away, returning to the main avenue.

I could feel the throb of the hangover in my left temple, stretching down to my jaw where I had the work done on my teeth a few years ago. I turned off into welcome shade, making for Edik's grave. The track becomes a little overgrown there, weeds pushing through the sparse gravel, sycamores arching together. It was quiet, the only noise the twittering of the birds and my own heavy breathing, the slight scuff as I dragged my right leg. And then, abruptly, I had the sense I was not alone.

I slowed, not out of fear or anything silly like that, more out of politeness, a respect for decency. I didn't want to intrude, sweating and red-faced, on a private grief. I mopped my brow with my handkerchief. The heat really was infernal. Was it getting hotter, or did old men just feel it more? I caught my breath and, slowly, pressed on. I desperately needed a drink. Water, coffee, vodka, anything. I turned the final corner and there, kneeling by Edik's grave, hands clasping the low metal railing, she was.

A woman in a light coat, grey hair pulled back from her brow into a loose bun. I stopped and as I did so she became aware of me and looked up with, well, what exactly? Guilt? Maybe that's to read too much into it. Regret? But it seemed less that she didn't want to be disturbed than that she didn't want to be seen there. She tossed a single bright red rose down on the pile of fading flowers and stood, straightening her coat as she did so. I knew then. I'd never met her, never seen her, but I knew.

She visibly set herself, a slender, upright figure, and walked quickly towards me. 'Marina!' I said but, head ducked, she brushed past and kept walking.

'Marina!' I repeated, but by the time I turned round, my old legs creaking, she was gone, a pale flicker in the shadows, and soon not even that. I paused for a moment, wondered if there was anything I should do. But all I could do, all I had ever done, was my job, and so I took the plastic sack from my pocket and with a sigh crouched down by the grave and set about clearing away the dying flowers.

The fresh red rose, I carefully lifted and set to one side to replace when I had done.

....

This is not about me, but I should introduce myself. I am not a writer. I am not a footballer. I am, I suppose, what you might call a functionary in that, in some lowly way, I make the club function. I have, over the years, swept the dressing-rooms, I've collected litter from the terraces, I've painted the stand, I've laid out the kit. Mostly I've fiddled about in the office. But none of these are my job as such. I am just Ivan. Vanya. I am there, as I have always been, and I do what is needed.

My father was a mechanic for ZIL – or ZIS as it was then before they took Stalin out of the name – and took me to Torpedo as a boy. I had polio when I was very young and although I recovered it left me with weakness in my legs. Even now I limp. I was an awkward child, couldn't join in with games, got tired easily. But I loved Torpedo, I loved the players and I loved the angry, funny men who watched them. When I was twelve, still at school, I started doing odd-jobs about the club and, having no desire to work in the car-plant like my father, I never left. The factory didn't want me with my gammy leg. Even during the war, I stayed, helpless to do anything else. And I enjoyed it. I liked being around the club, feeling useful. I worked in football, and not many could say that.

Not that you want to know any of that. You don't want to know my regrets. You want to know about Eduard Streltsov, the greatest footballer I ever saw – Edik, as we all knew him. I'm old now. I know that. And I know that we old men like to talk about the past, not because it was better then but because we understood it. Or more of it at least than we understand now. As I write these opening words, Russia – Russia, not the USSR – have just come back from the Euros in England. A great team, they said, but then they went out in the group. Great forwards. Kolyvanov, Kiriakov, Karpin... please. I have seen a great forward, and they are not that.

But at least they went to England. Thirty years ago, Edik did not. He could not. He was out of the gulag by then, still great, but they couldn't take him to the World Cup. We, the USSR, came fourth. But think of that side, not with Banichevsky, not with a kid from Azerbaijan, but with Edik. Might we not have beaten West Germany in the semi-final? He only scored one goal, Banichevsky. One goal in the whole World Cup, and that was against North Korea. One. Edik couldn't have played so many games and scored only one goal, not then. Even at his worst, even in his periods of dislocation and disaffection, he scored goals. Or he did until... but that was later.

I must stop this. I must stop thinking of what might have been. And I have to stop thinking of him only as footballer. As Eva always told me, you cannot judge a man only by the goals he scores.

After I got back from the cemetery, I had a drink with Misha, who has been my friend longer than either of us can remember. He is cleverer than me, more energetic, more ambitious. He ascended greater heights, has grandchildren now who are the age we were when we first met. I told him that I had seen her, or that I thought I had.

Being Misha, he was sceptical. 'Was it really her? How could you possibly recognise her? You never even met her then, did you?'

And he was right. I hadn't. Just photos.

I was sure in the cemetery. But it's hard to be certain about anything any more. It's not just about erratic memory, or my fading eyesight. The older I've got the more I've realised it's impossible to know anything for sure. Nothing is ever quite as it seems. Our senses and our reason lie to us just as readily as the government. All that is solid melts into air.

But I thought it was her, I did. And that was enough excuse for us to spend the afternoon telling the same old stories, exchanging the same old anecdotes, drinking the same beer and vodka and pausing every now and again for a tea. 'Write it down,' Misha said. 'Don't tell me who knows it already, tell them. Tell the people who didn't know Edik.'

And so I have. This is his story.

Or, more accurately, and I shall try to be accurate, these are my memories of him and this is my version of his story.

Глава вторая

1953

TORPEDO

Soviet League: *P20 W11 D3 L6 F34 A34 Pts25*. **Final position:** *3rd of 11 (MVO withdrew)*.
Soviet Cup: *Lost in quarter-final to Zenit Kuibyshev.*

We were only there for one reason. Normally I wouldn't have bothered with a friendly, not a game like this with the youth team, unless they'd asked me there specifically. Even I can have too much football. And to be honest, round that time I'd fallen into a habit of sitting at home by myself with the radio and the papers and a nip or two of vodka. I'd become self-conscious about my limp and didn't often relish company. But they said this kid was special, so Misha dragged me out. They said he was really special. Streltsov. Eduard Anatoliyevich Streltsov, Edik, the boy who would fascinate me for the rest of my life. He disappointed me and broke my heart, but I loved him always. He was the greatest player I ever saw.

Vasily Sevastyanovich Provornov, our youth coach, was excited and he didn't get excited by much. He tried to hide it, of course, but you could tell. His friend Mark Levin, who coached the youth team at the Fraser factory, had said he had three lads we might be interested in. But we all knew that Streltsov was the one we were really keen on. He was sixteen, big for his age, technically sublime, a star in the making.

Or that's what they said. We'd heard it before, of course. Football is full of prodigies. They're always the greatest thing ever. Faster, stronger, younger, more skilful. The hardest shot you ever saw. But football makes you cynical. You stop believing in heroes. I don't even mean the interference, the political meddling, the stupidity. I mean that people are disappointingly normal, that the hype is rarely justified and even when it is it soon wears off. Nothing takes off the shine like familiarity.

Yet I think we sensed this one might be different. I stood behind our goal in Plushchevo with Misha, hoping to be enraptured but expecting disappointment. The teams gathered for kick-off. I stared down into the other half. Where was he? A big blond lad, we'd been told, but I couldn't see him. There was Yevgeny Grishkov and there was Lev Kondratiev, the other two targets, but where was this Streltsov?

I turned to Misha but he was talking to an old guy from the Fraser factory. Misha was always talking to people, always getting information. He was good at it. Good at talking to women, too. Or good at talking to one woman in the office, at least: Eva, with the pale hair, the pretty nose and the good heart. Maybe it was her who told Misha to stop me wallowing.

Streltsov, Misha learned, had been selected for Fraser's first team, who were playing in Perovo. Their game had kicked off earlier and the plan was for Streltsov to race back here to join the game as soon as he could. My first reaction, I admit, was anger. This was absurd. How could they make a boy play 90 minutes with the men, and in a factory game that was sure to be brutal, then cycle back across Moscow and expect him to perform well in a trial with Torpedo? I thought of leaving there and then, but it was a warm afternoon and Misha had a flask. There are worse things to do than stand in the sun and watch football with a friend.

And so it was that the first time I saw Edik, he was skidding his bike to a halt by the touchline, cheeks red and blond quiff falling forward over his forehead, his boots knotted by the laces around his neck. He had a huge grin on his face and I think, had Levin let him, he would have come on there and then. But Levin told him to calm down, to change into his boots, to catch his breath and to take his place at the beginning of the second half.

Misha and I walked round to the other end of the ground at half-time, passing by the teams as they prepared to come back on. I looked out for him, of course. That dramatic arrival, the way he had leapt from the saddle, was enough to give a sense of his magnetism. He knelt slightly apart from his teammates, quiet and calm, fiddling with his boot. It would probably be too much to claim I saw something then of the reserve many took as self-possession but it was clear, I think, that he had already outgrown this team. The sense of anticipation was rekindled.

It didn't take long to see that he was special. There are the things you quickly learn to look for, things that anybody who watches football can see. He was quick, he was strong, his touch was exceptional. His body did not look like that of a sixteen year old. It was as though he belonged to a different, better species. Then there was the stuff Provornov and the coaches would talk about. His movement. His awareness. The intelligence of his runs. Did he feel the game, did he smell it? I would not pretend to be a specialist but it was obvious that he did. He was the sun around which the game revolved. In ten minutes, Misha and I were convinced. He wasn't just good, he wasn't just a promising kid we should take on and try to develop: he was great. Even then, I think, we wondered if he might be the greatest. I'd never seen anything like that in a boy so young.

But there was something else, something that is hard to explain to those who didn't know him then. He was a pure phantom. He had grace, despite his bulk. He moved with the litheness of some great cat. He had that blond hair that kept falling over his broad, handsome brow. Back then he smiled, a lot. He was the best player on the pitch by a distance and it was easy for him. At sixteen, he was dominating a game against young players who had been trained at a top club in some cases for years, and he was doing so while operating within his comfort zone having already played a match that day.

People have asked me since if he scored. Honestly, I don't remember. He must have done, for he always did back then, but I can't remember a goal. I just remember the sense that we had one, our own Fedotov, our own Bobrov.

Sure enough, the next day came the confirmation: Provornov had signed all three of them.

....

In those first weeks after Edik joined, our coach Nikolai Morozov asked me to find out more about him. Or more accurately, he asked Misha, and Misha got me to help him. He did the charming and the talking to neighbours, his father's former colleagues and his mother, the formidable Sofia Frolovna, and I looked through the records and pulled everything together into a report. It wasn't like later, when managers seemed to do full psychological profiling of players, but even then we understood it was good to know what was going on in their private life, especially when they were so young.

Streltsov had been born in Perovo, out to the east of Moscow, in July 1937. His father, Anatoly, was a carpenter who worked at the Fraser factory. He was gifted with his hands, making all the furniture in their home and developing a fine reputation at the factory. And he was gifted with his mouth, talking a number of women into situations that got them both into trouble.

I'm not sure his father and mother got on. Sofia Frolovna was tough, determined, inspirational in her way, but I doubt she was easy. Who knows what really goes on inside a marriage? But there was a story Edik would tell about his father to demonstrate his *sang-froid* that says a lot more besides. They were arguing one day, his mother and father, and

Sofia Frolovna took up a hot coffee pot from the stove and hurled it at her husband. He merely held out a huge hand and deflected it into the wall, then lit up a cigarette. 'Calm now?' he asked.

Anatoly was not a well-educated man – he'd completed four grades – but he was smart. He went to war a private and he soon became a scout, in which I'm sure his composure and courage were important assets. He came home on leave in 1943 accompanied by an orderly he'd met at the front. The orderly let slip that Anatoly had another woman in Kyiv, so Sofia Frolovna told him never to come home again, an instruction he appears to have accepted with relief. Anatoly lived in Kyiv and Sofia Frolovna remained in Perovo, resolutely alone, too proud, too determined never again to be duped by a man, to remarry. I lost my own family in the war, my father and brother at the front, my mother of grief soon after. The club became a home and a family and a life for me and perhaps it would have done for Edik had it not been for his mother. I have no wish to be cruel, for no one, least of all someone who has never been a parent, should criticise a mother's love for her son, but she influenced him, directly and indirectly, in ways that were not always useful.

They were poor, Sofia Frolovna and Edik. He would play football for hours in the yard and then run inside, suddenly starving, only to find there was no bread to be had. His mother had a heart attack while she was still young, suffered from asthma, and struggled physically, but she kept working at a kindergarten and then at the Fraser factory, where they found her a job I think out of sympathy. Edik worked there as well. He completed seven years at school and then got a job as a gauge maker. And it helped of course that he was so good at football.

First he played for the kids' team at the factory. I heard all the usual stories. How he'd first kicked a ball at eighteen months and how he spent every possible second playing in the backyard, barefoot in the sawdust, how all the neighbours had wearied at the constant thudding of the ball but had known then he would be a great. When you work in football, you hear these stories twice a week. But with Edik it was true.

When he started with the kids' team he was the smallest in the line-up, but he still played centre-forward, still burst through challenges, still hammered the ball into the net. And that I think shows the fallacy of what many who saw him later thought, that he was a player of brute strength. He wasn't. He was a footballer, with pace and understanding and balance, with skill. And then, in 1949, he grew 13cm, and suddenly he had strength and power as well. But he was not a player who relied on his physical assets; rather those assets magnified the player he was at heart.

Almost immediately, they picked him for the men's team of the plant, even though he was thirteen years old. When the team got together afterwards in a café, they would give him three rubles and tell him to go off and get himself an ice cream because they didn't want him hanging around when they were talking about men's affairs. You think of how he became, that strangely distant attitude, and I wonder if that was part of it. What childhood did he have? He was helping his mother from an early age, was taken away from boys his own age to play football with adults. He played the man's role at home but had no man to learn it from. He probably copied other players, but the dressing-room is no place to learn domestic responsibility.

He didn't see his father after the war until he was seventeen, after the death of his grandfather, who was a milling cutter at the Fraser factory. They buried him at Ilinka and at the funeral some kind of fight broke out. I don't know the details but somebody attacked Anatoly with an axe, a big man with murder in his eyes. His dad just laughed, stared at his attacker until he calmed down and then lit up a cigarette. Or that was the story Edik told. Maybe it was true, maybe he just wanted to think of his father's coolness and found a story to demonstrate it that didn't also involve his mother being humiliated.

Edik seemed to idealise his father. He would talk about how much he looked like him, joke about how his father had kept his hair while even in his late teens his own was showing where it would recede. His relationship with his mother was strained at times, which is natural when they were as dependent on each other as they were. He knew she had made great sacrifices to bring him up, but there were occasions when I think he resented her decision not to remarry. Another income and their life might have been a little easier. A male presence at home and his life might have been different.

What role model, really, did he have? Older footballers? By the time he knew them he had outstripped them. He had this idea of his dad, this tough, unflappable man who outsmarted the enemy, who boldly went out on reconnaissance missions, who casually ended one family and began another, but when you don't see him for fourteen years, how can it be said that you know him? And by forging his own way in the world, he ended up less bound by the conventions of society than the rest of us. Talent gave him licence, but it was a licence that existed already within him. I don't think we even knew the word dissident then, but that was what he was: not politically – he had no interest in or understanding of politics – but socially. More than anybody else I ever met, he refused to let the rules restrict him.

Edik's life was the factory and football. When he wasn't playing he would go into Moscow to watch league games, queueing for hours for the schoolboy tickets. He watched Dinamo and the CDKA of Fedotov and Bobrov, and he loved them of course, learned a lot from watching them. But the team he supported was Spartak.

It's hard to explain now with everything that has happened but Spartak were always a little different. Yes, there's a lot of rubbish talked about the

Starostins, who may have been rebels but were never the martyrs people like these days to pretend, but we used to say in those days that Spartak had democracy. They were a team. They passed the ball when it needed to be passed. Nobody at Spartak, Edik once said to me, thought himself a hero when he scored a goal. He wanted to play for them. Even after he had become established with Torpedo, Spartak was his dream – and that, I think, was for that vague ideal they represented.

Глава третья

1954

TORPEDO

Soviet League: *P24 W8 D6 L10 F34 A34 Pts23.* **Final position:** *9th of 13.*
Soviet Cup: *Lost in fourth round to CDSA Moscow.*

You grasp at the details and they slip away. This is what age does to you.
What you think you know it turns out you have constructed later often
from misremembered or misinterpreted details. Did you ever know it to
start with, or did you just read it? Are you remembering what happened
or what Misha told you happened? I have only fragments. That winter, I
know, Maslov left to work at the FSM, the new project to promote young
talent. We were sorry to see him go. We liked Viktor Aleksandrovich. I
don't think anybody then realised what he would become, the success he
would have in Kyiv, but he'd played for the club for years. He understood
Torpedo, and he treated the players like an uncle. We got instead another
former player – that was how it was in those days: Nikolai Morozov. He
would have his success at the World Cup in England, so you look back and
think we were very fortunate, little Torpedo, to have had such managers.
But Morozov at the time felt a step backwards.

So, yes, Nikolai Petrovich arrived in that winter of 53-54. Edik started
playing for the reserves and they went off to the south, to Batumi on the
Black Sea coast, for pre-season. He must have impressed there, I think,
because we played a tournament in Gorky and he was in the team. It was
terrible, a bad idea. I remember the cold and the snow, huddled in the
stand in a huge coat and hat thinking how absurd it was to expect them

14

to play in these conditions. At half-time we gave them glasses of port to warm up. You should have seen Edik's face, the shock of it! Port, in the dressing-room! He was not a drinker then. And I suppose he must have played well enough because when we went down to Kharkiv for the first two games of the season – that was how it was, you started the season in the south because it was too cold in Moscow – he was on the bench.

First we played Lokomotiv, the local side, and we won, easily, 4-1. Valentin Ivanov, Kuzma, scored twice. Morozov gave Edik 20 minutes or so at the end. Then we had our "home" game, against Trudovye Rezervy, from Leningrad. They were 1-0 up at half-time and got a second just after the break. That was typical of Torpedo: up and down, loose at the back. But then Edik came on. Vitaliy Vatskevich, who'd been the third top-scorer in the league the previous year, got one back, and then, six minutes from time, Edik put pressure on Alexander Dontsov and he knocked it past his own keeper: 2-2. We went on to Georgia to play Dinamo Tbilisi and I wondered if Edik might have done enough to get a start.

I remember thinking constantly on that train journey about whether Morozov would pick him. He'd changed the game against Trudovye Rezervy, but he was sixteen. It would be a huge call for a manager to make in his third match. And we had recent history with Dinamo, as you probably remember.

Or maybe you don't. That is something else age does: you assume events that loomed large in your life matter also to those born three or four decades later. Anyway, the previous season had been a great scandal. Stalin had died earlier that year and that meant Lavrenty Beria, the Georgian who had been head of the NKVD, was no longer as powerful as he had been. Beria was a great Dinamo Tbilisi fan – and he'd swung things in their favour against Spartak in 1939. But that, really, was before my time. Who knows what was going on? What I do know is that suddenly it became important to people who never usually cared about football that Dinamo

Tbilisi didn't win the league. They beat us, and some of our fans attacked their dressing-room. The game itself had been fine. The captains signed the protocol to ratify the result. Then from nowhere it was announced that we had lodged a complaint and that it had been upheld. Usually these things take months to resolve but this was done overnight. It was obvious they wouldn't be allowed to win. We even got Nikolai Latyshev as referee: he always favoured Moscow teams and we won 4-1. If they'd got those two points they'd have finished level at the top with Spartak and there'd have been a play-off for the title. It wasn't about us and it wasn't about Spartak, it was about making sure a team from Russia and not one from Georgia won the league. But you can understand why there was resentment.

Ten days earlier, Spartak had played in Tbilisi and lost 2-1 to Dinamo. I don't think we knew the full details at the time – I'd have been a lot more anxious if we had – but there'd been rioting in the streets around that game. This was as tough an environment as you can imagine for a kid to make his first start.

And Dinamo were a good side. Avtandil Gogoberidze, the inside-left with his little moustache and the lock of hair that fell over his forehead like a film star, had been the league's top scorer the previous season with Nikita Simonyan. "Basa", they called him, and he'd been called up to the national side a year or two before. They'd hammered us 4-0 last time we'd played there. Even without what had happened the previous year, the crowd there was always something special, passionate in a way you didn't get further north. Nobody went to Tbilisi in those days expecting a result. But Edik seemed totally unconcerned, sitting looking out of the window with that little smile on his face. How many trains had he taken in his life, never mind one for two days south through Ukraine, through Rostov and down the Black Sea coast? But he was like a veteran, calm, content in himself, uninvolved in all the usual banter and the practical jokes.

Morozov did pick Edik, putting him on the right wing. But it was like games always were down there. On their sort of pitch, hard and dusty, with the crowd behind them, they were very hard to stop. They had great skill in the forward-line, always, and once they got on top of you they dribbled you to death. It seemed like the usual story. We went 2-0 down. Morozov went out to the touchline and started gesturing at Edik. I thought he was taking him off. That's the way, isn't it? You pick a kid, he can't quite get in the game, and he's the one you sacrifice. But he didn't. He just told him to switch wings. You saw immediately the lift it gave him, as if he realised at that moment that his manager actually believed in him. He started running at opponents and terrifying them. They'd thought the game was done and suddenly here's this blond tank charging at them. Then it happened. Edik got the ball, brushed through two of them, nutmegged a third and lashed the ball with his left foot into the top corner. The goalkeeper Vladimir Margania didn't move, just watched it fly past him. The power was incredible. Of course we came to know that ability, but to see it for the first time, in that moment, well, that was something incredible. There was a pause, a moment of hush, and then the fans in the stadium applauded.

They always loved Edik in Tbilisi after that: that was their brand of football, played with panache. I remember one April a few years later, lashing rain, and 3000 of them tuned up for a training session just to watch him. The ball would roll out of play near them and he would go and collect it and they'd all applaud. Touching, I suppose, in its way, but you could see Edik felt a little uncomfortable. Whatever they said about him later, he never revelled in adulation. He wasn't a star in that sense.

We won 3-1 away at Krylya Sovetov, were starting to put a little run together – which we could do in those days. We'd finished third the previous season. We were a good side. And then came Edik's first game in Moscow, against Lokomotiv at the Stalinets in Cherkizovo. In my mind there was an air of anticipation about the game, a Moscow crowd keen to see one of their own, but the older I get the less I trust my memory. But the goal... the goal I remember clearly. Edik took the ball from Kuzma, knocked it forward and ran on, barged the defenders out of the way, one, two three, boom: 1-0! I found myself laughing spontaneously and I think most of the stadium did as well. There was something preposterous about how easy he made it look, this game to which so much thought was devoted reduced to charge and wallop.

It finished 1-0 and the boy was a hero. But there had been an incident that we maybe should have paid more attention to. Edik got involved in a running battle with their centre-back Gennady Zabelin, a tough guy with gingery hair. Morozov ended up taking him off so he didn't get sent off, and everybody dismissed it, especially when Zabelin tried to teach the kid a lesson in the return game, planted his studs in Edik's chest and found his leg being driven back into his body. He was like a bull, we said, a giant, indestructible, our superhero. But maybe we should have asked why he'd got himself into the spat in the first place.

Maybe that's why Nikolai Petrovich was sceptical about Edik, I don't know. Maybe he thought it was too good to be true, wanted to make sure his own expectations didn't run ahead of themselves. Edik scored four goals that season, and that was often playing on the wing. We'd never seen anything like it, not from somebody that age. I started cutting out articles that mentioned him from newspapers and magazines. But in his written report at the end of the year Morozov rated Edik's potential as less than that of Vatskevich. Unless he was trying to keep Edik's feet on the ground it was ludicrous. We could all see what we could see.

Fans started going to the stadium, whichever city we were in, just to see Edik. They wanted to believe just as I did. And perhaps it's only fair to acknowledge the extent I wanted this to be true. That first game in Plushchevo had kindled something in me and after what he did in Cherkizovo I was aflame. I would volunteer for jobs at the training ground just so I could watch him. I look now at the statistics and I see that we finished ninth that season, when we had taken the bronze medals the previous year. Perhaps I'm projecting the greatness that was to come, investing his every touch with the knowledge of what he would do.

When I think back, it is true that there were games that season when he did nothing. There always would be in his career but there were more of those nothing games then. He was sixteen. He would drift off, as though his mind were elsewhere, wandering around indifferent to the game. But perhaps there I have fallen into a fallacy that I cursed others for. One of Edik's problems was that he made the game look at times so easy that people thought he could just score goals when he felt like it. They spoke of him being "in the mood". But what did that mean? That goal against Lokomotiv looked simple, but it was the result not only of his pace and strength but of his sudden awareness that the opportunity was there, that if he pushed the ball into that space with just the right amount of power then there was a chance to accelerate through on goal. Sometimes the pieces simply didn't fall that way, the disposition of Edik and space and opponents wasn't right. And sometimes he wasn't right, the connection and the understanding of the field wasn't there. And in truth, he had too free a spirit to have much sense of duty.

I think of his understanding with Ivanov, how Edik and Kuzma would combine to overwhelm a defender – and in those days, you must remember, everybody played with three backs, so it was much easier to isolate one of them than it became. Kuzma scored seven goals that season. Anybody could see the effectiveness of their partnership – and they were good mates back then as well. But when I really think, when I try to be as honest as I can be, it is true that some of the veterans carped about Edik. Who did he think he was to demand a special role in the team, to complain when they didn't pass to him? He may have had the skill and physique of a player ten years older, but he was a sixteen year old and he had a frankness born of naivety. Perhaps there were times when he was too honest, when he could have recognised his status in the group, could have done more to dampen any jealousy they may have been feeling. Sincerity, we liked to call it, with all the ironies bound up in that concept. But all players come eventually to have a sense of their own mortality, they feel sooner than most age sapping at their powers, and nothing alerts them to their encroaching redundancy more abruptly than a brilliant teenager who is frustrated at their limitations and unable to conceive that his powers too will wane.

And the facts are there: Torpedo did worse that year, much worse. Was that Streltsov disrupting the balance? Or was it that Morozov was not Maslov? Fine coach though he was, Nikolai Petrovich lacked Viktor Aleksandrovich's genius for tactical organisation. At this remove, I cannot say. But what is true is that for those of us who believed, the boy offered plenty to justify our faith.

Most of all, perhaps, there was that final game of the season, at Dinamo Moscow. They were two points ahead of Spartak and needed a draw to confirm the championship. We had lost to them 2-0 at home earlier in the season and we seemed always to struggle to score against them, as though Lev Yashin were so great as to be unbeatable. Which was part of his greatness, of course: the dark sweater, the aura he had, it affected forwards mentally. I always thought he was a better goalkeeper psychologically than he was technically. We went behind very early, the first minute I think, but then midway through the half, Edik took the ball along the top of the box. The defence followed him, trying to deny him room for the shot, but

Kuzma stood still so that soon he was left in space. Edik backheeled the ball and Kuzma slammed it into the top corner. Dinamo were so rattled we scored again a couple of minutes later. They came back and won it 3-2 to take the title, but that backheel, stripped of context, lived on, cementing in the minds of the public the idea of Streltsov as a brilliant maverick, a player of great imagination who wrote his own rules. He'd never practised the backheel, he'd never talked to Kuzma about that move, it all came spontaneously. But from then on, Edik was associated with the backheel. That was his trick.

And it would be wrong to suggest that Edik was somehow at odds with the rest that season, that the tension with the senior players was anything out of the ordinary. Dressing-rooms can be cruel places. You have to develop a thick skin and a sharp tongue to survive. They teased him and he began to tease them back. He always had that distance but there were times when he revelled in it. You could see him blossoming.

But there were times when he would daydream and drift away from the action and his teammates would curse him and the crowd would grumble because they wanted him to give them a glimpse of the wonder to which he alone had access. The public can be very demanding of genius.

All of these things are true. And that complicates the picture. It would be easier to believe in the simple narrative, that 1954 was the year of his debut and development. But it's more complicated than that. It's more complicated as well than his faults being simply those of a kid. We all know teenagers are inconsistent, that you cannot expect them, even nineteen year olds, to play at the highest level week in, week out, that when you thrust one suddenly into the adult world they will be gauche and cocky, they will struggle to find the right register, and perhaps especially those who have grown up without a father. But many of the faults we saw that year were the faults he also had as an adult – his detachment, his occasional self-absorption, his impulsiveness. These were not flaws he would grow out of.

Perhaps if I had written it all down then it would be clearer and we would know what Edik was as a sixteen year old, without the filter of what we know now. Or perhaps not. Life is not an account book. Two good games and three bad ones and sorry, sir, you're in debt. Perhaps the more general impression is the truer one. Four decades on, my memory of that summer was of him laughing, the great head thrown back, his face lit up by that broad grin. And he always said he never had such fun as that first year, when everything was new and exciting, when each game was a fresh challenge, before all the expectation and everything that entailed. One last summer of childhood that he happened to spend playing football in the Soviet Supreme League, his final months of innocence.

Football takes over your life in different ways. First there is your love for it. It becomes your mistress. You play it or you watch it and it leads you on like the most capricious ladies of the old romances. It offers beauty and fulfilment but disappoints you and frustrates you and just often enough it yields a moment of pure delight. Then, if you work in the game, there is your club, which makes demands of you, shapes your life. Go to this game, but not to that one. Find us a new mower but not too expensive. Buy enough white paint for the stand but not a pot too much. Write a report that is comprehensive but no more than two pages long. Or play on the left today. Cover the half but support the wing. I experienced both aspects, fan and employee, different of course to a player but not entirely dissimilar. And how I dreamed of being a player, imagined how hard I would have trained, how I would have relished the camaraderie, the victories, the girls. But then, for the likes of Edik, there was more. His country, the government, the fans, the public, all trying to get their piece of him, celebrating his success but demanding it too. I watched it happen. I had seen it before and I saw it again but never quite as quickly, as intensely as it was for him.

Once the public had hold of him, they never let go. Whom do you blame? Journalists for exaggerating his achievements? The people for loving him too dearly? Edik for struggling to live with the adulation? It was an addiction. They needed their shot of Streltsov every week. And that didn't just mean watching him for what he was. They needed his genius. An ordinary goal or a little burst past a defender would be celebrated as further evidence of his greatness. Hyperbole became the only language in which he could be discussed. And so expectations were inflated, and so too the disappointments when he only occasionally attained heights that to anybody else would have been unscalable.

Football is a game that accommodates many sorts of genius. There are those who play with furious intensity, who set off at the referee's whistle and don't stop until the referee blows for the end of the half. And there are those who after long periods of inactivity burst suddenly into life and in one moment change the game, the afternoon, the week, the season. Edik was one of those. There were games when he did nothing. When he was like another spectator and the team was playing with ten, and then, in a flash, he had transformed the result and our perception of the game, transformed what we believed to be possible.

Always there was this criticism of him for standing still, for not getting involved. He heard it, precisely because he was so often standing still. But his idea, he always said, was to conserve energy, so he could suddenly pounce, so he could, as he liked to put it, "ambush" a defender. We all saw him do it. But there were other games when there was no ambush; there was just waiting.

And of course he had flat feet, or said he did. Certainly it's true that there were times after games when you'd see him hobbling, his muscles screaming at every awkward step. Others would say that it was because he wasn't fit, that if he'd spent more time developing his running it wouldn't have hurt him so much to run. I don't know, I'm not a doctor. His teammates rarely seemed to mind. And perhaps rather than picking faults it's better just to say that's what he was. That was the package, for good or for bad, and really, in terms of football, who of us would have changed anything?

As an athlete, perhaps, he was not Bobrov. But as a footballer, his movement, his understanding of the game, those explosive bursts… he was on another level. And he was stronger than Bobrov. There was a game against Dynamo Kyiv, I don't remember which year but before 1958, when Vitaly Golubev grabbed Edik's shirt as he went by and was dragged along behind him, trailing on the grass. Edik's shot hit the post but Kuzma turned it in – a day when the body and spirit were both willing.

I think of the game today, I think of Lobanovskyi and his "universal players", working and pressing. Edik was of a different school. Malofeev, perhaps, could have used him. Or he could, perhaps, if an accommodation with Bobrov could have been found, in the end have been the Spartak player he had wanted to be. But even Maslov, who did work with him so understandingly, I think would not have been able to use him in Kyiv after he had begun the great overhaul of our understanding of the game. 'Only Andriy Biba,' Viktor Aleksandrovich used to say, 'has full rights of democracy.' But Biba was more a team man than Edik, worked harder, kept his position in the organisation.

And the crowds got frustrated, of course they did. They went to the stadium and waited and waited and sometimes they were rewarded for their patience, but sometimes they were not. And sometimes they got enough that they could pretend they had seen the true genius. Edik felt that expectation. It weighed on him. How often did I see him ask to be excused a game, say his legs felt heavy? But they would get him out there. Maslov would coax him gently, others would push him out onto the field. And sometimes, after he had complained vociferously that it was impossible for him to play, he would catch light in the first minute and burn till the last. And sometimes he would disappear into himself.

At times I wondered if he avoided the ball because the cost of creativity was too great, if there were afternoons when he preferred not to take up his brush rather than risk making a clumsy mark on the canvas. He wouldn't speak of that. Ask him about one of his peripheral games and he'd laugh and say that in summer it could be very hot or offer some other banal excuse. Even if he had been willing to open himself, I doubt he'd have been able to articulate his struggle. Which of us really can say we know ourselves? But there is no doubt to me that his gift became at times a burden.

It made things difficult for the club as well. There was a day when they changed the date of an international friendly at the last minute. Torpedo had sent the players home and then suddenly they needed them again. Edik still lived out east, in Perovo where he had grown up. When we went to the camp at Myachkovo along the old Ryazan highway we would pick him up at the seven-storey building, a local landmark near his house. So this day they thought they would just send the bus to pick him up.

But of course Edik had no telephone and nobody could get hold of him. He didn't know the club was looking for him. The bus got to the seven-storey building and, what then? They asked somebody on the street where he lived and tried to follow the directions, circling round and round, asking more and more people, getting contradictory information, going up and down those narrow little streets, getting more and more frustrated, Nikolai Petrovich stalking up and down the aisle getting more and more irate, telling the dirver to leave him and then changing his mind while the players tried not to giggle. Eventually, after two hours, they found his place. But he wasn't there: he was out dancing at a party. What a warning sign that was.

That was embarrassing for the ZIL party and executive committee and the impetus for them to relocate Edik to Avtozavodskaya, nearer the others. He ended up in the same building as Ivanov, Edik on the sixth floor and Kuzma on the second. By then, Sofia Frolovna had fallen ill, I think, although the precise details are lost to me, and Edik was able to support her.

And, of course, the other reason for them to move him was control, to keep him away from his old friends who took him to parties. But they didn't lead him to sobriety. What a road that is, the alcoholic highway. Was it predetermined? Who knows? Was he drinking even then, back in Perovo? People liked to say that it was fame and football that brought him to drink, but I think back always to the frantic phone calls round a community where phones were scarce, the officials in their ZILs traipsing back and forth through his village. At the time we laughed, at least when he'd been found and the solution of a flat in Avtozavodskaya had been provided, but that afternoon was a precursor of so much of what was to come. Whether it was true then or not, he soon came to like alcohol, or perhaps to need it, and he loved parties, and especially the women who went to them.

Глава четвертая

1955

TORPEDO

Soviet League: *P22 W10 D8 L4 F39 A32 Pts28.* **Final position:** *4th of 12.*
Soviet Cup: *Lost in first round to Spartak Minsk.*

Soon the question was not if Edik would play for his country but when. I confess, I was not entirely easy about the prospect. Of course, I wanted him to have the recognition and, more than that, the opportunity to play on the greatest stage. Already, I think, we were beginning to look forward to the World Cup in Sweden. But I also knew that when he played for the USSR, we would lose another part of him, that he would stop being ours. There was, yes, a feeling of jealousy. And perhaps also, far below that, I feared for him. I knew how he suffered already from the adulation of fans but at least with Torpedo we could to an extent protect him.

Nikolai Petrovich was stern but he understood him. He had watched him grow. He knew Edik was in many ways still a child. What if Gavriil Kachalin, the national manager, just saw a giant? What if he didn't understand his talent? What if he didn't understand him? But the coach wasn't the biggest problem. Coaches learn. Coaches do what brings results and if they do not they move on. It was everybody else, all those suits and uniforms that stood behind Kachalin.

But it would be wrong to say the doubts were anywhere near the surface. I had them, yes, but with hindsight they are easy to magnify. Fundamentally, I wanted our boy to play for our country, because it was the best thing for him and for the team. I saw, beyond that surface of wry calm, how much he wanted it. His father had served his country as a scout; now he could do it on the football field.

The national team was strong then, even after the disaster of 1952. Gavriil Dimitriyevich played the political game well, but he was also an excellent coach. In September 1954 the USSR smashed Sweden 7-0. Later that month, we drew 1-1 with Hungary, who had lost in the World Cup final that summer but were still probably the best team in the world with Puskás, Bozsik, Kocsis and the rest of them. A lot of the names who would go to the Olympics in Melbourne were already in place: Yashin and Netto, of course, but also Bashashkin, Tishchenko, Tatushin and, most significant for Edik, the centre-forward Nikita Simonyan.

The following February, a tour was arranged to India to play three games, in Delhi, Mumbai and Kolkata. Kachalin picked an expanded squad and Edik and Kuzma were both included in it. It was a strange feeling. On the one hand they were delighted but the games were only 30 minutes each way because it was thought the Indians lacked the stamina for a full match. Large crowds turned out – I think I read more than 20,000 for each game – but everybody knew this wasn't real football. This was no challenge. The biggest tests were the heat, the pitches and the food. Kuzma played in Kolkata, but seemed fairly downbeat about the whole affair when he got back, while Edik didn't get a game at all. I suppose there were good reasons for the trip, but an aggregate 10-0 win with very few changes to the line-up all seemed a bit of a waste of time from a football point of view. Edik said nothing, but he must have been frustrated.

But fate finds a way. There'd been another game against Sweden arranged that June, away in Stockholm, at the Råsunda where the World Cup final would be played three years later. A little preview, we joked. Simonyan – who you must remember was an excellent player, he just wasn't Edik – was injured. So at 18, Edik got his chance, although there was no place for Kuzma.

There was a beautiful picture in the paper the next day that I cut out and kept for a while. I can still see it now, even when so much else has gone, Edik with his cheeks puffed out just beginning to turn back, in front of him Boris Tatushin, his left arm just completing a punch of celebration, the ball in the bottom right corner, the net still rippling, the goalkeeper Kalle Svensson, feet planted, staring at a defender who is just entering the left of the shot. You sense the shock of one of Edik's sudden eruptions, the relief and delight of his teammates, his casual awareness of his own genius. When there has been a clamour for a player to be called up, the fear is always that it takes him time to settle, that the sense of expectation brings almost unbearable scrutiny. We've all seen journalists counting up each passing minute in which the new boy hasn't scored. If they were doing that for Edik, they didn't even get to four. By half-time he had a hat-trick. Whatever reservations I may have had were overwhelmed by the sense of vindication. We won 6-0 and Edik came home a star.

....

That summer Edik met a girl and, for I think the first time, felt serious affection towards somebody. She was called Alla and she lived out on the Perovsky highway. It was a romantic story in its way. Her aunt had been Edik's teacher at kindergarten and they'd later gone to schools in the same building. They met again in the winter at the Perovsky club when Edik was 17. He'd noticed her but was surrounded by his friends and by the time he'd plucked up courage to abandon them and go and talk to her the bell had gone for the evening film to begin. Finally, soon after that game against Sweden, they got talking to each other at a dance at Linden Park in Perovo.

She didn't know anything about football. She had no idea he'd just scored a hat-trick on his international debut. And for him, I think, that was part of the appeal. She liked him not for the goals he scored or for the glory he might bring, but for who he was. She didn't see a centre-forward. She saw a handsome boy with blue eyes and a blond quiff and a diffident manner. And he saw somebody who could take him away from football, who didn't approach him with all those expectations. Although she did have certain expectations, the expectations any girl should have of any boy, and in the end he failed to live up to them.

I can't imagine they had much of a courtship because he was always away for matches and training camps. They went to the cinema sometimes and they would walk for miles through the woods in Perovo, Kuskovo and Plushevo. For him, at that time, she represented peace and calm away from the clamour of the stadium. I think they often stayed out quite late and that would cause problems with her mother but my impression at the time was it was all very innocent.

Or at least I thought it was. But then in August Edik missed a 3-2 win over West Germany because of a mysterious illness. When I asked Dr Sergey Yegorov, the club medic, about it, he just gave one of his half-smiles and said, 'our young hussar has been overly frivolous.' That was how he spoke, all allusion and riddle so you never quite knew what he was talking about, but the meaning seemed clear. Maybe we overestimated Alla's innocence, but more likely Edik was more active that we perhaps realised, and that the young love with Alla was not quite so pure as it may have seemed.

Edik was worried that his illness would count against him, but I'm not sure the national coaches ever realised what it was. Or if they did, they understood the wisdom in keeping it quiet. Edik was back in for a home game against India, which mattered far more for what it said about Kachalin's plans than for the game itself. But he scored three anyway, in an 11-1 win. Two games for his country, two hat-tricks.

There was a 1-1 draw away to Hungary, then he scored again in a 2-2 draw against France, although he was playing inside-right that day alongside Simonyan. Kuzma might have played but he had damaged his knee in a trial game a couple of weeks earlier. But while I felt sorry for him, mostly I felt joy for Edik, this boy who had come from nowhere and given us all hope.

Глава пятая

1956

TORPEDO

Soviet League: *P22 W8 D7 L7 F40 A37 Pts23.* **Final position:** *5th of 12.*
Soviet Cup: *Not played, to allow focus on Olympics.*

Others might have seen reasons for cautious optimism after 1955, when we finished fourth and Edik was top-scorer, but the bosses didn't. Too many draws, they said, which wasn't totally untrue even if the reaction seemed excessive. Nikolai Morozov was sacked and they appointed instead Konstantin Beskov. We know now what Beskov became, his feats with Spartak, his long struggle with Lobanovskyi, the Cup he won last year with Dinamo, but this was his first job in coaching. We knew him just as a centre-forward, and a very good one. But Beskov was, well, how can I put it? He wanted to impose himself. We know what he was like later at Spartak, when Yuri Morozov resigned as assistant coach after just a few weeks rather than be humiliated by Beskov in front of the players, and Yevgeny Lovchev quit the club rather than play for him. Imagine that sort of approach then, when Beskov was nobody, and when he'd arrived from a playing career at Dinamo? He wanted Edik and Kuzma to play in a certain way and, well, there was conflict.

It all started well. There was a draw against Shakhtar and a 4-2 defeat to Dinamo Tbilisi, but we'd won our other three games – and scored goals by the hatful – when we faced Spartak at the beginning of May. We were brilliant that day and beat them 2-0. There was a story told – I have no idea if it was true – that Nikolai Starostin, Spartak's great president, came up to Anatoly Maslenkin – a very good defender, who'd been the hero of the win against West Germany – after that match and started criticising him. 'Look, Tolya,' he said, 'how well Boris Khrenov played against our Simonyan, first to the ball...'

Maslenkin interrupted. 'Yes,' he said, 'I could also have played well against Nikita.'

Now Nikita Pavlovich, lovely man that he is, wasn't going to stand for that, and started reminding him of all the times he'd beaten him in training, but Maslenkin was right. Simonyan was a great forward but that day Edik was unstoppable.

I started to think that maybe it could be our year. But the euphoria of that day actually made things worse. Edik and Kuzma thought they didn't need Konstantin Ivanovich haranguing them constantly. Not that we knew at the time. Beskov never said anything specific. Edik and Kuzma got on with playing and training. They clearly respected the player Beskov had been.

But when you work around a club sometimes you smell something in the air. One morning I went into the office and found Misha and his wife Eva, with Vera, the ancient secretary, and maybe one or two others, crowded round the desk of Denis, the accountant. He'd heard from Mikhail in the ZIL directors' office that Beskov had proposed transferring Edik and Kuzma and the bosses were considering it. As soon as I heard, I felt a cold sensation in my chest. It was one of those pieces of bad news you realise you sort of already knew but your brain had somehow resisted putting it all together.

I was unsettled all day. This felt fundamental, the loss of something profound. We had, at our little team, the greatest player in Russia. And we had for him the perfect partner. Together they could have brought us the championship. And then they were going. Both of them.

I didn't sleep at all well that night, got up a couple of times and had a splash of vodka to try to calm my racing mind, but it was no good. This dream I'd had was dying. I told myelf it was only football, but what did I have other than football? I got up early the next morning, exhausted, my jaw aching where I'd ground my teeth. I had a quick wash, aware of the smell of stale sweat coming off me, shaved hurriedly, and left. For hours I walked about, smoking, trying not to think, watching Avtozavodskaya come to life, the bakers, the trams, the men on the early shift at the factory. I got my shoes shined at the kiosk run by Liza, an energetic little woman with dark eyes who, despite being a Spartak fan, was a great friend of a number of Torpedo players; they say Slava Metreveli once proposed to her, but I have no idea whether he was serious.

I wondered if I should try to find another job, which was an absurd thought. Torpedo and ZIL were my life. I found myself at the club, long before I needed to be there, went into the office with a sense of dread. There was an unreality to it all, Viktor at the gate, Yevgeny sweeping the driveway, everybody going about their routines with this catastrophe mounting. I went into the office and said good morning to Vera. Was she always there that early?

'Beskov's gone,' she said.

I felt my legs lose strength. I left the office to try to find somebody who might know what was going on. I saw Vadim, the kit man, carrying a basket from the laundry. 'Vadik,' I shouted. 'Is it true?'

'So they say.'

I crossed the yard and by the gate I met two journalists just arriving. They'd heard the story as well. Denis had let them know. But they had more.

'Have you heard who's replacing him?'

I shook my head.

'Viktor Aleksandrovich.'

Maslov! Maslov was back! It was perfect. He was perfect. Grandpa would look after Edik. I went back and told the office and you could sense the delight. Everybody liked Maslov.

....

In retrospect, I don't think it was all about Edik and Kuzma. They were young and, while Edik might not always have followed instructions, he wasn't somebody who would have kicked up a fuss. And at the time, their focus was more on the national side. The Olympics had come to dominate their thinking. They wouldn't have got involved in politicking at the club. Beskov was a great coach but he was a harsh man and he had fallen into conflict with some of the veterans at the club. The issue of Edik and Kuzma became a useful symbol for those veterans and helped to turn opinion against Beskov.

And Maslov was far from a step down. He was a genius, although at the time football hadn't quite appreciated that. Rather he was loved. He was a legend at Torpedo. And he was, fundamentally, a lovely man. He projected warmth. He listened to people. He had a great ability to remember not only your name but your circumstances. He saw Misha, he would ask about his son. He saw Vera, he would ask about the grandchildren. He saw me, he would talk about the old days at Torpedo. Some criticised him for drinking with the players but his idea was always better one drink with him than ten that he didn't know about.

But you shouldn't make the mistake of underestimating Viktor Alexandrovich. There were plenty who thought him a soft touch who learned that. He could be tough when he needed to be. What he did exceptionally well was to make the players feel confident. He never criticised them individually after games. He would make general points but players felt they could make mistakes without facing a rollicking in the dressing-room afterwards.

And almost without you noticing he made tactical changes. He didn't go as far as he would in Kyiv, but he dropped Yuri Falin back to give us an extra man in midfield. That allowed us to control games a little more and when you have a strike duo as potent as Edik and Kuzma, it didn't really reduce our attacking capabilities. In 1956 we finished fifth, 11 points behind Spartak – which made you think of that 2-0 win in May and how, again, we had wasted a great opportunity with our inconsistency.

....

But that year, really, was about the Olympics. Finally, in May 1956, Kachalin had picked Edik and Kuzma together and they both scored in a 5-1 win over Denmark. Even more encouragingly, there were signs they worked well with Spartak's Sergei Salnikov, who got two that day. Simonyan played away in Denmark but in September, for the return friendly against West Germany, Edik and Kuzma were together again, with Tatushin, Ilyin and Salnikov across the forward line. This was clearly the side Kachalin wanted to use at the Olympics three months later.

They were so worried about defeat the game wasn't even broadcast. All we knew about it back in Moscow were a couple of clips on a newsreel, but that was enough. What a sight! 90,000 in the stadium in Hanover, sunshine, the pitch like a carpet. And after three minutes, a low ball through from Netto, a little acceleration from Edik and a finish under the keeper.

Then, well, you shouldn't say it, but I never thought Lev Yashin was quite what they made him out to be. Yes, he was good, very good, but they needed a hero. He was a good party man. He had an aura. He played for Dinamo. He had big hands and great presence; he looked like a goalkeeper should. But he made mistakes and this was a bad one, just a couple of minutes after Edik's goal. I'm not a goalkeeping specialist, but it was obvious to me that he was flat-footed, so had to dive to take a cross he should have been moving his feet for. He hit the ground hard, spilled it and Willi Schröder knocked it in.

But nine minutes before half-time, Ilyin swung in a corner from the left, it was half-cleared and came to Tatushin on the right side of the box. He waited just a fraction to draw Fritz Herkenrath from his goal then squared it and Kuzma ran in just ahead of Edik to tap it over the line. We won 2-1 and to listen to Kuzma and Edik afterwards was to know how well we had played. Suddenly they were thinking they could achieve something in Melbourne: and if you can beat the world champions, why not?

Football, though, isn't a logical game. We struggled to build on that result in Hanover. Hungary by then were nothing like the side they'd been two or three years earlier. Gusztáv Sebes had gone and Márton Bukovi had come in, which was a definite upgrade from a pure football point of view, a tactician for a politician, but it was also indicative of the chaos that had gone on there since they'd lost in the World Cup final. As it turned out, with the Uprising a couple of months later, it was pretty much the end for that team. Anyway, they won 1-0, the first international played at Luzhniki, and then the following month we went to Paris.

They dropped Kuzma, and we lost 2-1. I think that French team, with Jonquet, Piantoni and Mekhloufi, was maybe better than we'd realised – although Kopa and Fontaine were missing – but there was panic. So because the suits never understand football, because they always think it should be controllable and that you should be able to guarantee wins, after a training camp in Tashkent and before the squad got on the plane for Melbourne they made them all go to the Sports Ministry and swear they'd lay down their bones to win Olympic gold. Ridiculous! As if they wouldn't have tried before. Imagine Edik giving an oath like that! I can see him now, trying to keep the smile off his lips as he said whatever pompous words they told him to say. And with Edik trying was never really the point.

I had followed our first Olympic Games in 1952, of course I had. I read the reports in the newspapers and knew about our best sportspeople. I celebrated like anybody else when Nina Romashkova won her gold medal in the discus. But for those of us who loved football, everything was overshadowed by those games against Yugoslavia: to draw having been 4-0 and 5-1 down was incredible, and evidence of the greatness of Bobrov, but then to lose the replay... We knew straightaway it was a catastrophe. It would have been bad enough against anybody, but to Yugoslavia, the way the politics were with Tito at the time, well, that couldn't be allowed.

I was at the club, helping Eva compose a letter when Misha came in with the news: CDKA had been disbanded as some sort of punishment for the defeat. We can say now that it's absurd. You cannot give yourself to a football match. It's a sport that can always bite you, against any opponent. And that was a good Yugoslavia – Mitić, Bobek, Zebec, great players... Of course you can't guarantee victory. People in football knew that, but that's how it was in those days. You didn't say anything.

But I followed the Olympics more in 56. We didn't have a player in the side in 52, although Agustín Gomez was on the stand-by list. Remember him? He was a left-back, played for Torpedo for a decade. He was a Basque who'd come over to escape the Civil War when he was a kid. He captained us for a while, led the team that won the Cup that year, nice little player. But in 56 we had two, Edik and Kuzma. It was a squad full of Spartak players, really, but they didn't have two forwards like Edik and Kuzma. And of course, if you picked one, you picked them both, so close was their relationship.

The games were in Melbourne so for those of us in Moscow they kicked off early. I would go into the office long before dawn. It was November, so it was always cold and we'd sit around a heater in the office, about half a dozen of us, eating bread and sausage with the samovar bubbling. We'd have the radio on, listening to the commentary. They're some of my favourite memories, those mornings, the windows steamed with condensation, that sense of togetherness with the other boys, joking to hide our nerves, waiting.

In the first round we beat Germany, who had a strange team, a mix of professionals from the GDR and amateurs from the West. We won 2-1, comfortably enough, I think, although we lacked fluency against a well-organised side that defended deep. Edik got our second to make it 2-0 with about five minutes to go before they pulled one back. But there was a lot of talk about the forward line not quite functioning, about our Torpedo lads not quite gelling with the Spartak players.

The assumption was that they'd sort themselves out against Indonesia. As the game went on and still we hadn't scored, it seemed not quite real. We assumed we had to score at some point. But we didn't: 0-0, against Indonesia. A club had been disbanded for losing to Yugoslavia four years earlier. In a football sense, losing to Indonesia would have been a hundred times worse, and Misha said they were allied to Tito politically. Times had changed since 52 but you couldn't help but be anxious. Fortunately we beat them 4-0 in the replay – although that game kicked off at three in the morning so I didn't get up for that. Furma got a goal, and there were three from Spartak players – two for Salnikov and one for Netto.

Which meant Bulgaria again. I tell myself I am not superstitious, that omens and foreshadowing is the empty chatter of peasants, but everybody in football believes in them to an extent. In a game that can otherwise seem so random, it's a way of imposing order. We have studied the opponent, we have trained hard, we are ready, but we should also pay obeisance to the deeper powers just in case. And we all know those games when you can just feel that it will never go in, when you just have to accept that destiny was against you. So, yes, Bulgaria worried me. And they always played well against us.

Nothing. For a long, long time nothing. Bulgaria resisting us, again. 0-0 at 90 minutes. Was that game a little later? I think it was. I recall watching rhomboids of faint sunlight on the desk by the radio as the game went on, focusing on them to ease my nerves. What do I remember from the time? What have I filled in from what I read in the newspapers and magazines, from what Kuzma and Edik later told me? I don't know. I know they had Australian Rules football at the main stadium so our game was pushed to the smaller ground across the road. Why would I remember that? And then there are the details everybody knows. Nikolai Tishchenko, our right-back, broke his collar-bone. He had it set and returned to the field, but he was a passenger on the wing. Then Kuzma hurt his knee. He stayed on and limped around, but really we were down to nine. It was impossible. All we could do was to try to see out extra-time and hope for a replay.

But five minutes into extra-time, Ivan Kolev, who always scored against us, scored against us. It was done. It was over. We had to attack, and that suited the Bulgarians who liked anyway to play on the counter. And now they were breaking against nine men. All chance of the gold medals had gone and all we could do was hope the repercussions wouldn't be too severe.

Then Anatoli Bashashkin, who had been captain four years earlier and had been at CDKA, hit the ball long out of defence. Edik charged through the middle. Bulgaria had defenders back marking Tishchenko and Ivanov and they converged on Edik. Later, Edik said that Kuzma had feinted and that had momentarily distracted his marker and only because of that did he have space. He ran through, him against Georgi Naydenov (you might remember him, CSKA Sofia's goalkeeper for years; he died very young, in Damascus, poisoned – they said – by the Interior Ministry, one of those dark stories you heard in those days). Naydenov was good, very experienced, a master at reading players. And he read Streltsov. But as Edik took his shot, the ball bobbled and he mishit. Naydenov was wrong-footed and somehow we were level.

Four minutes later, Vlada Ryzhkin, who was rapid when he got going, played a one-two with the injured Tishchenko, which of course Bulgaria didn't expect. He got away down the left and Boris Tatushin from Spartak headed in the winner. It was exactly the same pattern as four years earlier: Kolev after 95 minutes then two goals in four minutes to win it. I celebrated, of course I did, but at the same time I had a sick feeling in my stomach. Back then, fate reacted almost straightaway. This time it would wait two years before taking its revenge, not only on Edik, but on Tatushin as well.

And who was it in the final but Yugoslavia again? Kuzma was too badly injured and couldn't play and then the day before the final we heard that Edik wouldn't either. There was some nonsense about him drinking too much water and being tired after so many games in the heat, but I think Kachalin had decided that Edik and Kuzma came as a pair. And maybe in those days it was true. So Anatoly Ilyin played instead of Kuzma and Nikita Simonyan replaced Edik, meaning the whole of the forward line was from Spartak.

I didn't bother with the final; I was too disappointed for Edik, frustrated with Kachalin. I read the newspapers the next day, of course, but my enthusiasm had gone. We won, at least, and that was something. They never found much rhythm but they had enough and Ilyin got the only goal with a glancing header just after half-time.

In those days only the eleven who played in the final were given medals. Simonyan was a good man, an Armenian, not just a great forward but later a great manager as well. And he knew that he didn't really deserve his. So in the dressing room after the game he went up to Edik and tried to hand it over, telling him he deserved it. Which was typical of him. But Edik's response was typical as well. How can I explain to people who didn't know him? He was 19. He looked at Nikita Pavlovich who was 30 and decided this was probably his last chance, so he told him to keep it.

Edik was a kid. He thought he had all the time in the world. He assumed there would be other tournaments and he wanted a medal he had earned by playing in the final.

Some thought he was arrogant but it wasn't that. He just had a faith in himself. He had never failed on the pitch. Why wouldn't the success continue? He had no experience that would make him think otherwise. But he would never play in another tournament. In the national shirt he never burned brighter than in those final minutes against Bulgaria in the semi-final, his final minutes in a tournament, but he never burned again, not on the world stage.

They gave him honours back in Moscow. Or they sort of did. He got the Order of the Red Badge of Labour but for some reason Lev Yashin collected it for him. And he got the Order of Lenin but that was presented to the captain, Igor Netto. Perhaps even then they didn't trust him, saw something irresponsible or immature in his behaviour. And Edik and Kuzma were both named Honoured Masters of Sport. But a decade later, they'd have to give it to him again.

Глава шестая

1957

TORPEDO

Soviet League: *P22 W11 D6 L5 F46 A23 Pts28.* **Final position:** *2nd of 12.*
Soviet Cup: *Lost in semi-final to Spartak Moscow.*

The Olympics changed everything. Suddenly Edik wasn't just Edik any more.

Alla said she'd never seen Edik even tipsy until a celebration of the Olympic success at some boy's house. I don't know how true that was: he liked parties sure enough, but maybe he went for the girls not the drink. Maybe she was just making the point that he changed after the Olympics, started drinking more and more regularly. I think we all saw the change in him, even if we didn't like to acknowledge it. Then he got drunk again at a party in Myachkovo that winter, leading to their first serious row.

Early in January there was a ball to celebrate the Olympic gold. All the players were invited to a lavish event attended by very senior officials and politicians including the Minister for Culture, Yekaterina Furtseva. Is she famous now? It's so hard to know what people who weren't there at the time understand. She was famous then. She'd been a textile worker who'd risen to a position on Moscow City Council and had gained a reputation when she'd destroyed Boris Babochkin in *Pravda*. He'd been one of the most famous actors in the country, but she didn't like the way he depicted a Communist leader in some play or other and that was it, he never worked again. Khrushchev liked her and she became the second woman to be a member of the Politburo. Then there was that scandal when it turned out she was having a fling with the ambassador in Yugoslavia and flying off to meet him all the time but she kept her job for years. Anyway, she was a formidable figure.

There was a lot said about what happened between Yekaterina Alexeyevna and Edik later, most of it nonsense, but the gossip at the club the following day was quite simple. Yekaterina Alexeyevna wanted to introduce Edik to her sixteen-year-old daughter, who probably had a crush on him. A lot of girls did. At which Edik blurted out, 'I won't swap my Alka for anyone.' Which was awkward and socially embarrassing but it was also very typical of him. He was young and immature and there were times when his honesty and candour were almost pathological. Later there were all kinds of stories that Edik had called the girl a monkey or had said that he'd rather hang himself than marry her, but it was much simpler than that. He panicked that this girl, this daughter of an important politician, would have certain expectations and clumsily sought to head them off. Given how he treated Alla there's an irony to that. But I doubt Yekaterina Alexeyevna was bothered by it, for all the later conspiracy theories that she began plotting against him at that moment. Although I suppose it is possible that it confirmed in her mind some bad opinion of him.

But the significance of the ball wasn't just that conversation. It was that it was the beginning of a new life. Edik started getting invited to all kinds of functions, official and more informal. He became a public figure, with all the responsibility that entails, responsibility he wasn't equipped to handle.

....

The other thing the Olympics did was confirm to everybody how good the Ivanov-Streltsov partnership was, even if they hadn't played in the final. And for a club like Torpedo that was a problem. Even some of the ZIL leadership spoke publicly about moving them on to a bigger club. CSKA wanted to sign them; that was an open secret. For days it was the talk of the training ground. CSKA offered them each a two-room apartment and it looked like the deal would go through. I resigned myself to losing them. But then something happened. There was a delay. There were doubts. Edik kept asking questions. I think he knew, deep down, that the ZIL bosses would protect him in a way the army wouldn't, and I think maybe he realised from the persistence of the CSKA leaders that they would expect success immediately and consistently. So they stayed.

There were rumours about Spartak as well for a while. And maybe that was more appealing. Edik supported them. Nikolai Starostin would have protected him. And the Olympics had shown how well he and Kuzma fitted into that forward line. But to go there would have been to take Nikita Simonyan's place, and Edik couldn't bear to stab him in the back.

....

Edik's life was changing in other ways, too. He'd proposed to Alla before he set off for the Olympic Games and she'd said yes but wanted to keep it a secret because she knew her mother would think they were too young. But then they told Alik Denisenko, the goalkeeper, and within a few days, a few hours even, everybody knew. Edik's mother was furious at that, raging that the whole factory and the club had all been told before she had. Sofia Frolovna had a way of making it about her. It all seemed comical until you stopped to think about it. Of course she was upset, realising she was about to lose her son for this young girl she barely knew. Every time I come to write about Sofia Frolovna, I find I have to check myself. She was a hard woman. She was difficult. If she came into the club or to the stadium, we would all try to avoid her. Nobody wanted to be trapped listening to one of her rants or caught up in one of her schemes. But then you look at her life and you understand why. Abandoned by her husband, she had nobody apart from Edik, and Edik from sixteen was public property.

Edik was immature. You must understand that. Or maybe because of his talent, because of his physique, we expected him to be more mature than he was. Maybe he was just like any other lad of that age. He fell in love with a girl who offered him an escape, from football, from pressure, from the demands of his mother. Or he thought he was in love with her – who ever really knows, least of all a teenager being dragged this way and that by his mother on one side and fame on the other?

He asked her to marry him. And when people found out, it brought embarrassment and chaos. He was still only twenty. So he shut himself off from her. The Olympic celebrations were still going on. I think he didn't see Alla for a month. That's terrible behaviour, of course, cruel even, but he was somebody who at times struggled to recognise the impact what he did could have on others. I didn't know Alla especially well, but she seemed a sweet girl, pretty, bright as well. She worked for the chief designer at the Stalmost factory and later she studied at dental college. I liked her, what I knew of her.

It doesn't excuse him running away, but I don't really know how upset she was. I wonder if she began to realise that there was trouble attached to this relationship, if she were perhaps torn between her affection for him and her understanding of what marriage to him might bring. But anyway, in early February, just before the squad went off for spring training, Edik's mother telephoned her at the Stalmost factory and apologised. Then, on Edik's behalf, Sofia Frolovna invited Alla to go to see the Austrian ballet on ice. You never know how true these stories are, but the way I heard it – and we were all talking about it at the time – Alla asked why Edik hadn't rung himself. And his mother said he was right there next to her and handed him the phone. But he was so awkward he didn't say anything until Alla agreed to go with him.

Why did Sofia Frolovna do that if she was so – and the term is perhaps not quite right – jealous of Alla? I think because she saw what Edik was like without her. That January was the first time he really went off the rails, drinking and womanising. It wasn't just the argument at Myachkovo. His mother, I think, released that she could do a lot worse for a daughter-in-law than Alla and decided that Edik with her calming influence was a lot better than Edik without. Or maybe she just felt guilty. Who knows? People are never consistent.

They went to the ballet and, knowing Edik, he'd have struggled to say the right words, to offer the apology he owed Alla. He took her home – and he was living in Avtozavodskaya by then, so it was a long way – and was desperate for a kiss to show they were reconciled. But she never gave it. Young as she was, she was clever enough for that. A day or two later he was off to Kuibyshev for training. He got back, and almost immediately, at the end of February, they got married. It was all very rushed.

....

Maslov liked Alla. I think he saw her as a way of calming Edik down and providing him with some stability. Alla was around the club a lot in those days. I'm not saying the marriage was Viktor Aleksandrovich's idea, but he certainly wasn't against it. The big problem was Sofia Frolovna, so the club sent Dr Yegorov to try to talk her round with his riddles. In part it was because Alla came from a poor family. I think Sofia Frolovna had hoped her famous son would marry somebody who could help make her life a little easier.

But that wasn't the only reason. We heard the stories, a lot of them from Sofia Frolovna herself. There was a spell when she and Alla seemed to get on but she soon took to criticising her daughter-in-law. Edik would stay out late with his friends then go back home to Alla who would sit up waiting for him. She would shout at him and there were at least a couple of times when she slapped him. And could you blame her? He often seemed to regard her as an afterthought, a woman to go home to when he'd finished having fun. Those were different times, but even then that was a poor way to behave. And I know what he was like. She would have raged at him and he would just have stood there with that insolent half-smile on his face. Even if he had felt regret or sorrow, he would never have been able to articulate it. And Sofia Frolovna didn't like anybody else criticising her son.

Edik's relationship with his mother became more and more strained. He spent more and more time away from home. Twice he packed up his belongings and threatened to walk out. Then there was the night when Edik and Alla turned up drunk at the flat in Avtozavodskaya with Mikhail Ogonkov and his girlfriend. Edik had started to hang around with Ogonkov more than Kuzma and I'm not sure his influence was healthy. I know Kuzma got annoyed by it. Dr Yegorov had even warned Sofia Frolovna not to keep alcohol at home, to try to ease Edik's consumption. That night, Edik had phoned his mother from a bar to tell her they would be coming home in a few minutes. When they got there, she hadn't laid out wine and snacks and so Edik flew into a fury, stormed out in his stocking feet and ended up spending the night in the dormitory at the club. Mikhail Ogonkov and his girlfriend just went to sleep in the flat, and so Sofia Frolovna called Dr Yegorov. He went over and threw Ogonkov out – in the office we spent a long time joking about what convoluted words he would have used – a performance that gave him a certain standing with Sofia Frolovna from then on. And that, of course, gave us an additional insight into their world: the combination of Dr Yegorov and Vera was all the surveillance you needed.

....

Looking back that season was chaos from start to finish. How did we not see disaster coming? Why did we not take decisive action rather than shuffling the buckets under each new leak in the roof? The first game was away in Kishinev against Burevestnik. We played well enough and won 2-0, with Kuzma and Edik getting the goals. But after the game Edik got drunk in front of the bosses, which caused a lot of embarrassment. Not that it bothered him, of course. He wasn't the one who felt embarrassed. Five days later in Odessa he got the only goal against Spartak Minsk.

To an outsider, it must have seemed like everything was going well. He was married to a pretty girl and scoring goals. What more could a young man want? But we insiders should have seen the warning signs. But then, what could we have done? There were so many bosses, so many committees, who could ever have taken responsibility? Besides, the football always took priority – and the football was going well.

At the end of June, there was a friendly against Romania. Edik scored but the USSR didn't play well and it finished 1-1. We later found out that Postnikov had criticised the timing of his wedding in an internal memo within the Sports Ministry, said it showed how poor the educational work was at Torpedo. Well, it was easy for a suit to say that. It was an attempt to stabilise Edik. Maybe it was ill-conceived. Certainly it was rushed. And you can't claim it worked. Look, I've never married so maybe I don't know what I'm talking about but Edik was too independent. I don't think marriage was for him, not at that age. But at the time, what alternatives were there?

The situation as it turned out was absurd. Dr Yegorov used to go round to the apartment every day, worried that the tension between Sofia Frolovna and Alla would lead Edik to spend even more time away from home. Then one day Sofia Frolovna attacked him, accused the club of fawning over her boy rather than educating him, and so Yegorov stopped going back.

We all knew the marriage was a calamity. They would go out together to some dinner or other, and Alla would go home and Edik would stay out drinking with friends and his fans. And women. And that made the atmosphere with Sofia Frolovna even worse. Again, I admit, I know nothing of mothers-in-law, but Vera's theory was that Sofia Frolovna felt Alla had driven a wedge between mother and child, had weakened those bonds, but that Alla then was not strong enough to govern him. She had freed him from one source of control without providing another. And maybe that is true. Vera was both a mother and a mother-in-law, after all. But I wonder whether Alla was a useful excuse for Sofia Frolovna. She knew she had lost her son and it was easier to blame Alla than herself.

But Edik never played better than he did in the second half of 1957. Under Viktor Aleksandrovich, Torpedo were playing great football. On the pitch Edik seemed relaxed and happy. Perhaps by that point it was only there he could find peace. On his twentieth birthday, July 20, he played for the USSR against Bulgaria and scored twice. He seemed quicker and more powerful than ever, playing with obvious energy and joy, a player at home in his body and, it seemed, only just beginning to explore the furthest reaches of its potential. If he could keep this up, we all wondered, what might he be able to do at the World Cup the following summer? Assuming we qualified, that is, although nobody really doubted we would. We'd beaten Poland the previous month and, a week after the Bulgaria game, we beat Finland at home in a qualifier. All we had to do then was win in Helsinki and avoid defeat away to Poland and we were guaranteed our place in Sweden.

That summer they held the third edition of the International Friendly Sports Youth Games as part of the World Youth Festival in Moscow. As a competition it was nonsense, really. Other countries sent youth teams. We played our strongest XI and won the tournament. None of that meant anything. But Edik was brilliant. In four games against Hungary, Czechoslovakia, Indonesia and China, he scored six times. You almost wished he hadn't wasted those performances on games that didn't really matter.

Then it turned out Alla was pregnant and that just made things more complicated. She was very sick and Edik didn't have the capacity to cope. He just went on drinking and having his fun, while the bosses kept calling Sofia and Alla and urging them to get him under control. To people he didn't know he was charming, always there with his grin, but he had no sense of responsibility to those who depended on him. But by then you couldn't control Edik. Written down like that it looks bad, and I suppose it was bad, but at the time I'm not sure any of us were overly critical. He was just a young man doing what young men do: we didn't really think about his pregnant wife at home. And the culture was different then, after the War. Men and women, how men saw women… the War changed a lot. If we had a concern it was what his high jinks meant for his football. We failed him. I don't think we can deny that. But if Viktor Aleksandrovich failed him, I'm not sure who wouldn't have done.

And Sofia Frolovna failed her son. She treated Alla miserably. Again, I write it down like that and it looks so stark that I wonder if I'm being unfair, if all those years of trying to avoid her in the office and listening to the gossip prejudiced me against her. But her solution to all this was to give Alla a fifty-ruble note to go and get an abortion.

It was Vera who told us the story, a few weeks later. She became close to Alla at that time, tried to support her. Vera was always picking up waifs and strays to help. She was a kind woman, was very good to me after my mother died.

When Sofia Frolovna gave her the money, Alla left the apartment with just a string bag containing her dental textbooks. Edik lay on a couch facing the wall and did nothing to intervene. The first thing she did was to take the fifty and buy an ice cream. Then she bought Edik a gift. She was just a girl. She went back to her mother's and her mother told her that if the child wasn't wanted she should get rid of it. She had no support anywhere apart from her little brother. He asked her what she wanted to do and she said she wanted the baby. So he insisted to their mother that she should have it and keep living there, out in the apartment on the Petrovsky highway. She took paid leave so she could recover.

But in those days individuals couldn't just decide these things. All the committees from the trade unions and the ZIL factory got involved and they basically decided – correctly, I think – that Alla was the wronged party. They told Sofia Frolovna that she had to make her peace with Alla, and they gave Edik a new apartment, a bigger one, just opposite the one where he had been living, to try to help the marriage. And they took Alla there to meet Sofia Frolovna. A disaster! Alla turned up, there were lots of men from the committees there and Sofia Frolovna was agitated and started screaming. But Alla stayed.

What Vera told us... well, it's unimaginable. The poor love. She spent the money she got from her paid leave to equip the new apartment – pots, pans, everything. Maybe I'm being unfair – older men perhaps are prone to misunderstand such matters – but it felt a girl playing at house, doing what she'd seen the grown-ups do. And nobody gave her a thing. And young women kept arriving at the apartment, asking to see Edik. Often he would go off with them. The women who operated the lifts would stand guard, try to make him stay, but he would always find an excuse. It was shameful. Dr Yegorov spent a lot of time at the apartment at that time. He said Sofia Frolovna by then couldn't be even in the same room as Alla – or as he put it, 'she couldn't tolerate even a glimpse of our charming young vixen.'

The national team went to Helsinki and won 10-0. Edik got two. The team got back from Helsinki late on a Friday. Alla was asleep but Edik sat up with his mother talking. And she told him terrible things about Alla, said she never helped around the house, said she had been unfaithful. What had begun after a goalscoring trip to Sweden effectively ended after a goalscoring trip to Finland three years later.

Do I think Alla was cheating on him? I don't know. She was pregnant but nobody ever really knows what happens when the apartment door is shut. I know Viktor Aleksandrovich didn't believe she was. He said Edik was her first boyfriend. He thought this was just Sofia Frolovna's bitterness talking. Her husband had cheated on her, so it stood to reason that her son's wife must have cheated on him. That proves nothing, of course. There's plenty of middle-aged men been deceived by doe eyes and a demure aspect. Maslov tended to be a good judge of character – but pretty teenage girls are not young men on a football pitch.

Avtozavodskaya was like a big village. Everybody was linked through the factory. Everybody knew everybody's business. And by and large people there were on Alla's side. And she was pregnant. Then again, Sofia Frolovna didn't readily attract sympathy. Maybe Alla cheated because she was being cheated on. It wouldn't be the first time a desire for revenge had led to such a thing. But more likely, I think, is that Edik's guilt at how he treated Alla led him to accuse her of precisely the things he was guilty of.

None of that really matters. If Alla were guilty of any fault it was nothing beside his – except that women are judged more harshly in such things. Eva taught me that. But Edik believed his mother, perhaps saw in Alla his own faults. How much easier to excuse yourself if you can believe the person you are cheating is also cheating you. The next morning – this is the Saturday, a week before he scored at Zenit Leningrad in the Cup – he told Alla that he didn't love her any more, didn't want to live with her any more. Alla asked what she should do and he said he would pay for the child or pay for an abortion, whichever she preferred. So she left, but she appealed to Gavriil Kachalin, the national coach. So the usual committees convened, the factory, the Party, even the local Prosecutor, and Alla ended up being returned to Edik.

And still the goals kept flowing. I look back now and think that if only he had stopped playing so well, we might have done more to help. But he had a focus and a drive on the pitch at that time that made you think nothing could really be that bad. He scored two away against Spartak Minsk in the league and then three against a touring Nice side. At the beginning of September, Torpedo demolished Dinamo Tbilisi 5-1 and then Dynamo Kyiv 5-1 in the league – Edik was brilliant in both games and scored one in each. Then he got five against Dinamo Tbilisi in the Cup quarter-final. The club went on tour to France – not me, obviously; I wasn't important enough for that – and Edik scored hat-tricks against Marseille and Racing and another goal against Nice. They said the big French clubs wanted to sign him, but of course the authorities would never have allowed that – and nobody thought there was the remotest possibility he might defect. At the end of the month he got the winner two minutes from time as the national team beat Hungary.

But then a strange thing happened. I wish I could remember the details more clearly, but the memory has fragmented under the weight of everything that followed. We'd worked into the evening, trying to reconcile the budget for the following year, everybody irritable and smoking heavily, and then I'd gone to Misha's flat for something to eat. Eva, I remember, had fried up some cutlets; she was always a very good cook. It was just after the national side had lost away in Poland, which meant we needed to play them again in a play-off for World Cup qualification. I was tired, my leg was troubling me, and, yes, I was a little drunk, so I decided to take the tram home rather than walk. It was late. There was nobody about. Just one other person at the tram stop, leaning against a fence. I'd already acknowledged him when I realised it was Edik. Usually I didn't really speak to players much. I knew they liked their privacy. But this was one of those times when it would have been more awkward not to speak to him. We weren't friends or anything like that, but he recognised me, knew who I was.

He had also had a bit to drink. We chatted. I said how well he was playing, that it seemed like he was in the best form of his life. I found it hard to know what to say; how could I talk to somebody like that? They were leaving a couple days later to go to Ukraine for a game against Shakhtar and I probably asked something lame about whether he was looking forward to it. He sighed with a great sense of weariness. I must have looked surprised.

'I'm tired, Vanya,' he said. 'My legs ache, my body aches. They don't know how hard it is... every week...'

I didn't know what to say. I was tired. My leg ached. My body ached. 'You're young,' I said, hopelessly.

'Not in my head.'

I looked at him, silently. What was I supposed to say? His concerns seemed so banal, so trivial. He had such power and grace. And yet he seemed drained, propped up against the fence. I thought how absurd it was that somebody constructed like him should suffer from flat feet and I looked down at them in the yellow light of the street lamp.

'Nobody understands...' He sighed, gave a half-yawn and pulled himself upright.

But of course it wasn't his feet. His feet were just the thing he could blame. He seemed spiritually exhausted, and that worried me. He must have seen the look on my face. He checked himself and laughed, slapped me on the shoulder. 'We'll beat Shakhtar,' he said. 'Don't worry.'

And we did, 4-0. Edik scored twice. But I thought about that conversation a lot, later. Should I have asked him then about his home life? But what good would it have done? Who was I to challenge him? It wasn't my place. Why would he have listened to me, the bloke with the gammy leg who helped out around the club? And no man likes to think people are gossiping about him.

Four days later, he got the opener in a 2-0 win over Zenit, but later in the game took a whack to the calf that left him hobbling. In retrospect, that was when it all began to go wrong. But in 97 days, he had played 22 games and scored 31 goals. For three months, he was untouchable.

Mikhail Yakushin won the league with Dinamo again, but we came second. Kuzma scored 14 goals and Edik 12. We were young, we were exciting, we had hope. It was the most dangerous of times.

....

The last game in Moscow that season was played on a holiday, a Friday in early November (we had one more match to play down in Tbilisi the following month against Lokomotiv). Edik was left out to rest his injury before the World Cup play-off against Poland, but he turned up to support the team anyway. Amid everything they said about him after, always remember that: he loved his club and his teammates enough to come to cheer them on.

He was tipsy when he arrived. He kept drinking during the game, which kicked off at 7pm. Maybe that was a little embarrassing but, really, it was the only way he could bear the attention of fans – and of course they gathered around him.

Why did he drink? Why does anybody drink? Everybody drank in those days. Nobody thought of alcoholism as a disease. Footballers drank, all of them. Kuzma drank, Netto drank, Simonyan drank, even Yashin drank. Bobrov drank, and he had his scrapes as a result, but he was also able to deliver the most beautiful toasts at functions and so he was forgiven. And Streltsov drank more, a lot more and a lot more often. His mother would beg him to keep away from the vodka, but of course he didn't listen. Alcohol liberated him. Sober he was a shy boy. The attention of fans troubled him, all these workers from the ZIL plant wanting their piece of him, wanting to hear what he had to say, to glory in being in his presence, in the sense that he was one of them, some of them even to criticise him. He hated that, being denied his own space, the solitude he was used to and perhaps required, yet he knew it was inevitable, that this was the cost of talent, and that he in some sense owed it to them. Talent is to an extent always public. Sober he could seem distant, stand-offish even. With alcohol inside him, he was funny, convivial, charming. And so he drank to make his popularity bearable.

He had regret, of course. Who doesn't in the grey light of morning? The pangs of conscience are the worst part of a hangover. And he knew the risk to his talent. He never took his ability for granted, not in that way. But equally his talent was so great it gave him licence. He could play without training to the maximum, and coaches did not make the same demands on him they would on other, lesser players. You hear them say, 'Ah, but if he had not drunk how great might he been?' but that is to misunderstand him. The drink and the talent and the shyness, they were all related. Take away one element and you change the whole. The older I get the more I realise people just are, that perhaps we cannot change. Yes, you can try harder or live with greater discipline, but the capacity to do so is itself part of the character. Edik didn't have that, but he had so much else. Or perhaps that is to be too generous. But back then I inclined to sympathy.

We lost 1-0 to Dinamo but nobody was too bothered. They were champions, we were second, it had been a very promising season and that game was essentially a formality to be got out of the way. Following the match, they went drinking some more. After a while, Edik began to feel the worse for wear so he took the bus home. On the way, though, he found his enthusiasm for alcohol reawakened. That's where the story becomes a little murky. Edik decided to go and find some friends, although he seems unable to have been able to remember exactly which friends. Somewhere near his house, Edik met a neighbour of his called Galya Chupalenkova. She realised both that he was extremely drunk and that he was in no mood to go home, so decided to join him to try to make sure he didn't get into trouble. They took the number 46 tram, to the Farmers Market. By then, Edik was tired and Galya was able to persuade him to turn round and go home. So they crossed to the other side of the tracks.

As they waited for the tram home, a man started to bother Edik. He asked Edik about football and then, when Edik explained he was tired and asked to be left alone, he swung a punch that left Edik bleeding from the nose. Edik snapped. The man ran off and Edik gave chase, catching him as a he climbed over a fence, holding his leg so the man hung upside down. The man got loose and ran off again. Galya saw him go into a basement apartment, so Edik broke in, smashing plates and sending pots flying as he raged in the kitchen, demanding to see the fugitive. The residents, saying they had no knowledge of this man, and understandably upset at a drunk footballer shattering their crockery, called the police and Edik was arrested.

I learned most of this the following day. Normally I wouldn't have gone in on a Saturday unless it was a match day, but there's always little bits and bobs to do at the end of the season, stock checks to do, requisition forms to be filled out, player registration details to be confirmed – and there was always a nice atmosphere as well. There'd be a couple of bottles on the go, and Vera would bake a cake – like the end of term at school. But when I got in Misha wasn't there. Eva said the bosses had called him in early.

You could tell something was up from the way the bosses were acting. Normally a couple would come in for a drink but we just kept seeing them rushing about, looking stressed. And where was Misha? Then a rumour got about. It was Edik. He'd done something stupid. He'd been arrested.

It was afternoon by the time Misha arrived. He looked exhausted, his tie loose, his face drained. He took the vodka he was offered, knocked it straight back and held out his glass for another one. He sat on his desk and downed another vodka. 'It's Edik,' he said. 'He's a bloody idiot.' Misha had been called into the police station in the early hours while the bosses managed to ensure no charges were ever brought. He explained the whole story. The mood was grim. We all, I think, had the sense that this was a step into new and worrying territory.

Did that story make sense? That he just happened to bump into a neighbour, and she decided to escort him, to protect him in his drunkenness? Or was she another of his women? There were a lot of rumours floating about but people said Sofia Frolovna was trying to promote her to supplant Alla. Later, certainly, Edik wrote to his mother with messages to pass on to Galya.

Throughout that year Streltsov drank too much. There'd been instances when he'd been kicked out of the factory club for being rowdy. Once he'd even demanded Krylov, the factory director, be summoned to tell everybody he should be allowed to keep having fun. Maybe we should have paid more attention, but the tendency was just to laugh. He always seemed harmless.

But he was drinking more and more. We knew that. I thought back to that meeting at the tram stop. People tried to excuse it by saying that all he did was accept the drinks fans bought him, but that's too easy. In part because it's not true – although the free drinks didn't help – but more because he could have said no. He should have said no. He was an elite sportsman. And what happened in that apartment was inexcusable. That wasn't high spirits. For the first time, or the first time we knew about, there was a sense he was out of control.

Then came that World Cup qualification play-off against Poland in Leipzig at the end of November, a game that wouldn't have been necessary these days because we had by far the better goal-difference. But in those days if you finished level on points you had a play-off. The squad had been told to meet at the Belorusskaya Station to catch the overnight Berlin Express. Edik and Kuzma decided to have dinner at Kuzma's sister's and, of course, they drank wine. Maybe more, I don't know.

They could have caught the Metro – there's a direct line from Avtozavodskaya to Belorusskaya – but they decided to take a taxi. Transport could be difficult for Edik then given his fame. But they left too late, hit traffic, and arrived at the station just as the train was pulling out. It was unfortunate and careless, and it didn't help that they were a little drunk. The head of the Department of Football at the Sports Ministry – Valentin Panfilovich Antipyenok – was waiting for them on the platform. I can't imagine he was very happy, but he was able to call ahead and get the train to wait at Mozhaisk. Edik and Kuzma jumped in a car, raced off and caught up with the rest of the team. It was embarrassing, but essentially it shouldn't have been a big deal, particularly given what followed.

Edik was still feeling the injury but he realised that after turning up late he couldn't then withdraw from the game, so he went to Oleg Belakovsky, the physio, and asked him to patch him up so he could play. The Poles knew he was injured and – you can't blame them – made the most of it. Five minutes in one of them clattered him in the air and he landed badly, worsening the injury. Really he shouldn't have been jumping at all. Belakovsky bandaged him up because there was no alternative. And... he played brilliantly. Edik scored after half an hour and set up the second for

Henrikh Fedosov. Kachalin said he'd never seen him play as well on two legs as he did on one.

We'd made it to the World Cup and I think we thought then that arriving late would just go down as another Edik story. Remember that time he missed the train and then beat Poland on one leg?

I look back now and wonder if there was anything more we could have done. But I'm not even sure the two events were linked. He got drunk at the end of the season and broke into a flat. He got stuck in traffic and missed a train. The tendency, now, of course, knowing what came next, is to see the two events as part of a pattern but I don't know. I still don't really understand what happened the first night. The story never made any sense. And I don't understand why they were late for the train. Was it traffic? Were they just unlucky? Or had they drunk too much and lost track of time? Did they assume the train would wait for them? I don't know. All I can say is that we weren't asking those questions at the time.

Глава седьмая

1958

TORPEDO

Soviet League: *P22 W7 D8 L7 F51 A42 Pts22.* **Final position:** *7th of 12.*
Soviet Cup: *Lost in final to Spartak Moscow.*

'Has anybody seen Streltsov?'

I was completing a mandate to order more ink. A young man with a strict parting had come into the office. I didn't recognise him. But you could tell by his manner that he was rising in the Party and was on some ZIL committee or other.

'Anybody?' he asked again. 'When was the last time any of you saw Eduard Anatoliyevich?'

We glanced around at each other. It was early February. Nobody had seen him for weeks. It was the close season but you would normally hear something of players: they'd have visited the club doctor or been to the gym or popped in to sort out some registration or something. I'd been a little uneasy for a while, but what could I do? It wasn't like I could have gone round to his apartment or anything. Dr Yegorov knew nothing and so we knew nothing. I'd told myself not to worry, that a quiet spell was what he needed, that Alla was pregnant, but I sensed immediately that something was badly wrong. Nobody said anything. The young man glared at us. Misha, slowly, got to his feet and approached him. Misha was very good in those circumstances. He spoke quietly to the young man and guided him out of the room.

A few minutes later he came back in. He had that look about him I'd seen before: tired, resigned and determined. 'He's been an idiot again,' he said. He sighed and his tongue flicked along his lower lip.

He looked at Vera. 'Can you get Dr Yegorov on the phone?'

Then he turned to the rest of us. 'The day before yesterday,' he said, 'some girl turned up at Edik's flat in a rabbit-skin coat and asked him to go off with her. Alla kicked off, as she would, and the girl said that her brother was about to go on a trip and it was essential Edik went to see him off. He hasn't come home yet.'

I felt winded. Not concern for Edik, so much, although I suppose the possibility existed that he'd got himself in another fight and this time somebody had pulled a knife or something, but despair. How stupid, how irresponsible, could he be? His wife was expecting a baby and the squad was leaving for a training camp in Sochi in two days. How could he treat her like that? And, how could he treat the club like that?

Misha sent a couple of lads out on their bicycles to look for Edik, got the rest of us making telephone calls, trying to work out where he might be. When Vera got through to Dr Yegorov, it turned out he'd already been to see Alla, who was understandably upset. He'd asked her what she wanted and when she said, 'My boy,' he'd given her a doll he'd brought for the baby. He went back later and gave her some oranges to try to keep her healthy, but the situation was miserable.

We didn't find him that day. I went home late. Everybody went home late. There was an awful mood of tension about the place. The threat of what might have happened to Edik, the threat of what the Party might do because of our failure to control him. I didn't go straight home but walked about trying to think where he might have gone. I got up early the next morning and did the same thing on the way to the club. I was angry, not just for the stress he was causing everybody but for the sense of waste. To have a talent like that and to treat it like this. You could say this irresponsibility was another fact of the spontaneity that marked him out on the pitch, but there were limits.

He wasn't found that day either. Fury started to fade to anxiety.

Finally, early the following morning, they found him in a terrible state, washed up in a corner down some back alley, drunk and exhausted.

I think Alla was going to leave him but the very next day, he went off to Sochi for that training camp. Then Sofia Frolovna took Alla's keys and threw her out of the apartment.

The whole thing was appalling.

And yet still we gave him the benefit. We excused him. The pressure on him was so great, we said, that he sought relief where he could, that he buried himself into a soft, smooth body and for a time his troubles, the expectations, the burden of his talent fell away. Without a father, he relied more than most on a woman's love and as his mother became increasingly bitter and unable to provide that, he sought it elsewhere, in his string of girls. Which is perhaps to say no more than that he married too soon and having made the commitment found himself unable to live up to it. Alla could never be a mother substitute, or at least not then.

And he was still so young, so hopelessly unable to handle any of it.

But, as Eva said, the biggest victim of it all was Alla.

....

It was only on the Monday when he came in for training that we found out. There was a whisper went round the office that Misha confirmed soon enough. Edik had got himself into trouble again and this time it was hard to disguise. He had a black eye and a busted lip and, the lads told us later, bruises all over his body. Poor Misha had spent his Sunday at the police station trying to sort it all out.

In as far as anybody could work out what had happened – and given everybody had been drunk, that wasn't easy – it appeared that he'd got into a row at the Dinamo Metro station and punched – or maybe slapped, depending who you believed – a citizen called Ivanov in the face. Again the police had got involved, but this time they'd given him a going over back at the station. Did they know he was a footballer, that his body was his life? They must have done: everybody knew Edik. At least they left his legs largely untouched.

The bruises would heal, but this was an additional worry. It wasn't just that these drunken incidents were becoming more common, it was that whatever protection he had once had seemed to have fallen away. The club and the factory managed to hush it up, but the sense was that we could no longer rely on a blind eye being turned. There was even talk they were out to get him.

....

The snow was piled high, the wind was from the east and the sky the previous day had had that sickly yellow colour that suggests more snow is imminent. I was woken by a hammering on the door. For a moment I hoped it would go away but then it began again and I heard Misha's voice shouting my name. It was a few days after the fight at the Metro station. I wrapped a robe around me and struggled blinking to the door.

There were traces of snow on his hat and the shoulders of his coat as he marched past me. I'd seen this mood in him before, when fear or anger stimulated an intense energy. He marched to the far end of the kitchen and back, removing his gloves and hat. He took a newspaper from his pocket and thrust it into my hands as he removed his coat and hung it on the peg by the door.

It was a copy of *Konsomolskaya Pravda*, folded back to reveal the headline, 'Star Disease'. I felt immediately that pressure in my chest again.

I knew what this was about. It was another of those moments when you realise the bad news has been lying in wait and you've ignored it, hearing it, smelling it, knowing it was there but lacking the courage to whip back the curtain and reveal it. I sat down in the kitchen and with a trembling hand took a cigarette from a packet that lay on the table.

The article was written by Semyon Narignani. Maybe he wasn't the force he had been in the forties but he still a powerful figure, a poisonous writer, somebody they used to take people down. And *Pravda* was edited by Khrushchev's son-in-law, Alexei Adzhubei. It was a propaganda tool, same as it had always been, but there would be many, I knew, who would see the attack on Edik and think it was true, every word. To be criticised by the press back then was a very serious matter.

Over six pages – six! – the diatribe systematically destroyed Edik's character. It didn't dwell on the two fights, I suppose because that would have meant acknowledging that the police had bowed to the wishes of the ZIL directors in ignoring them, but on his supposed self-indulgence. He was a star, it said, and cared only for himself. 'Just three years ago he was a clean and honest kid,' Narignani wrote. 'He didn't smoke or drink. Blushed if the coach made a remark to him. And suddenly everything changed. Edik smokes, drinks and brawls. The wonderful boy has become conceited. It is no longer the Torpedo coach who gives him instructions, but he who urges the coach on.'

It had enough truth to be damaging. Edik did smoke and drink more than he should. He did get involved in fights. He had become more confident. The idea that he told Viktor Aleksandrovich what to do was nonsense, but then you wouldn't see him screaming at Edik, as Beskov might have done during a game. That wasn't Maslov's style.

Narignani dwelt on the missed train – understandably, for his purposes. Had Edik not disgraced his country by arriving late for duty? He invented details, said he and Kuzma had been at a restaurant and that they'd claimed they kept trying to leave only for another drink to be bought. It wasn't true, but it was believable. People did keep buying Edik drinks. He did struggle to say no. And the result was that even if he had the best intentions, he would end up drunk far more often than was wise.

The attack described with great drama the 90-minute race to Mozhaisk to overtake the train, the negotiations with the Railway Minister to have the Express make an unscheduled stop. And the way he told it, it was Edik and Kuzma demanding that the politicians should do these things. But imagine the alternative. Imagine if we hadn't qualified for the World Cup because the officials hadn't done these things and we'd turned up to a play-off without two of our forward line.

'Let him be a talent, let him score,' Narignani went on. 'But why was the all-Soviet Committee in a hurry to award him the title of Honoured Master of Sports? We have talented people in other fields besides sports — in music, painting, singing and science. But neither Shostakovich, nor Khachaturian, nor Tupolev, nor Ulanova, nor Richter, nor Dolukhanova were given titles at the age of nineteen. A football player should be rewarded not for a dozen goals scored in one summer, but for stable sports performance, not only for playing well himself, but for passing experience to his friends. An honorary title must be won, earned, and suffered through selfless labour in sports.'

To which the obvious answer was that Shostakovich, Khachaturian and the rest hadn't won Olympic gold medals when they were teenagers. But really this was playing on the familiar prejudice that football somehow was frivolous, that it wasn't worthy of recognition in the same way as the arts.

On one of their trips abroad, Edik and Kuzma had bought coats in the foreign style, with epaulettes. It meant nothing. They liked the look, no more. But even that was used against him. They said he liked to show off, that he thought himself too good for Russian styles. They even claimed he was a *stilyaga*, which was absurd. He never dressed like them, never spoke like them, never to my knowledge expressed any admiration for America or its music. Maybe that was a thing in the universities, but you just didn't get *stilyagi* at football clubs. There was no counter-culture in Avtozavodskaya.

But this wasn't about logic. It was an assassination, and it played on the idea of a young man getting above himself. There was an absurd line that Edik supposedly had said that he had experienced everything life had to offer, that he'd even eaten a salad for 87 rubles 50. The aim was to create an image of somebody so blessed with wealth that he would pay absurd sums for food that wouldn't even fill him up, to create an image of a life of excess and indulgence. (As Misha said, much, much later, you could probably get a deal on two abortions for that.) It was clever, for which factory worker, toiling every day for their modest wage, did not feel some sense that footballers had it easy?

Later the factory magazine *Vertigo* claimed it had written a criticism of Edik and his supposed excesses long before *Pravda* but had been forced to cut it by party officials. There were plenty of people who looked at sportsmen with their little luxuries, the two-room flats, the cars, the foreign travel, and felt jealous, even if they admired what they could do on the field or the rink or the track. But why should he not have a two-room flat? All the Spartak players in the national team did.

It also hinted, I think, at a truth, at a fear on the part of the authorities that Edik was not just a cog in the great machine. I've said this before. He wasn't disruptive but he did exist somehow apart from authority. He would listen to a coach, he wouldn't disagree with him, but he wouldn't necessarily follow instructions. He was a creature who followed his instinct. And as his fame grew, perhaps they feared what that autonomy might lead him to say or do. Did I ever think Edik was planning to defect? No, absolutely not. Quite apart from anything else, he just wasn't organised enough. Was it possible that he might have left his hotel one night in France or Australia or Sweden and not come back? To be honest, yes. If the whim had taken him, and he'd met a girl, he might have stayed. I don't think it ever was likely, and he wasn't in any way political, but it was possible. I always felt there was something within Edik, a recklessness, that nobody knew or understood, probably including him.

Narignani was clever. You can't deny him that. (Of course, he was acting under orders. As time has passed I have almost stopped hating him. Is it his fault he was so good at his job? He was the AK47. It was somebody else who pulled the trigger, Adzhubei acting on the orders of the suits. I realise that now. The question we should all have asked was, why then? Why make this huge fuss about the missed train two and a half months later?) Narignani spoke of those who, instead of loving talent, made demands of it. That was how it was then. It was as though talent was an obligation, that those who had it had to give more than the ordinary citizen, that effort was the price they paid for their gifts.

Narignani diagnosed that. Oh, he was sharp. But he was cruel. He didn't ask how to relieve the burden, he blamed Edik for feeling it. He said he stopped caring for his friends, stopped trying, stopped sweating, acted like a star too grand for the provincial stage, stopped behaving in the way a socialist society demands. But sweat had never been part of Edik's game. He accused him of going where his left foot dictated. Yes, that was the point! That was what made him great. And this word "star" kept coming up again and again. Viktor Aleksandrovich had used it, unfortunately, of Edik and Kuzma. Just an offhand remark: 'Yes, they're our stars.' But "star" meant Hollywood and glamour and the West and salads for 87 rubles 50. It meant standing out in a society that demanded uniformity. It meant not being incompatible with socialism. And it killed Edik.

He understood the alcohol as well. Narignani claimed that if you tried to take his vodka, Edik would shout, 'Don't stand in the way of my courage.' Which is nonsense, in that I can't imagine Edik ever saying those words. But the spirit of it was true. Edik was shy. He hated the attention. He hated the pressure and the expectation. And he shielded his vulnerability with alcohol. But alcohol made him unmanageable. It released a wildness in him that usually stayed far below the surface, suppressed by that reserve that, sober, seemed his true character.

After that, the target was on Edik's back. Other columnists, less talented, less astute, less sensitive than Narignani, joined in. They made up ridiculous stories about him. They said he was so unaware of the world beyond his immediate environment that he thought Sochi was on the Caspian and that he believed that the sea was only salty because fish swim in it. Crude, spiteful insults, words nobody could believe. But it didn't matter. Each drip wore away at Edik's reputation. To the wider public, he ceased to be a great footballer, and became an erratic footballer with an attitude problem.

They took away the title of Honoured Master of Sport after the incident at the Dinamo Metro station. Did he care? I'm not sure. It made it easier to justify some of the luxuries he was granted but it was essentially a piece of paper. What was more worrying was how it fitted a general pattern. The state was withdrawing its protection. By early 1958, Edik was exposed.

Narignani said that national team players had demanded the award be withdrawn by the All-Union Committee and had also called for Edik to be dropped before they flew off on a trip to China, that they'd told him to go back to his club, to work hard, to prove that he knew his actions had consequences, that they couldn't accept the drinking brawler who had replaced the clean-living and modest player he had been.

And it was true. There had been a meeting of the players at the building on Skaterny Pareulok where the Sports Committee was based. I heard they passed round a photograph of Edik showing him after he'd been beaten up by the police after that incident at the Metro and that some of the players felt it was a warning, or even that the suits were gloating over what they'd done to this young athlete. Postnikov, the first deputy, led the meeting. Edik was there and apologised to everybody. Kachalin tried to take some of the blame on himself and said he should have been stricter, suggesting as a compromise measure that the Honoured Master title should be withdrawn and that the stipend Edik received for playing for the national team should be reduced but that he should be allowed to carry on playing. A number of players, including Lev Yashin and Nikita Simonyan, agreed, but two – I won't say whom – thinking of their own position in the team, insisted he had to be dropped.

That was clearly the outcome that Postnikov wanted. Maybe he even put those two players up to their objections. He certainly guided them. Simonyan chaired the meeting and ended up signing the paper to say the decision was unanimous, but everybody in the game knew that wasn't true.

The immediate consequences weren't too significant. Edik didn't go to China and they took instead Vasily Buzunov who'd just rejoined SKA from Sverdlovsk. He had a hard shot but not much else and from what Kuzma said it was soon obvious that he wouldn't fit into that forward line. By the time the USSR played again, Edik was back in the side. The China tour had been a miserable experience for the players and they were keen to get back to some sort of normality. A letter of repentance appeared in *Konsomoskaya Pravda* with Edik's signature on it and that was enough. He was back. From a purely football point of view, it seemed his indiscretion had meant little. But this had ceased to be purely about football.

....

The 1958 season began in Odessa with a game against Zenit. It was supposed to be about Edik learning his lesson and turning over a new leaf, but of course nothing ever works out as easily as that. I was travelling with the team again at that time. Edik and Alla still hadn't reconciled. He was unsettled. He never said anything – certainly not to me, but you could see he was restless. He and Alla spoke on the telephone the day before the game and she told him she felt the baby was very close. He said he would rush back to Moscow to be with her, but we had to explain to him that was impossible. I'm sure he knew where Sochi was but there were times when he could be remarkably unworldly. The game finished 0-0 and that same weekend, Alla gave birth to Mila. We went on to Kishinev and, in heavy rain, Edik scored in a 3-1 win over Moldova.

At that stage it felt as though whatever else was going on, his form never suffered. From turning 20 in June 1957 right up until the season breaking for the World Cup a year later, he was brilliant. He was drinking too much, he kept getting arrested, he was constantly complaining about pain and the pressure, his marriage was collapsing and he had a new-born daughter, but whatever was thrown at him, whatever he brought on himself, he remained untouchable on the pitch.

Kuzma got a hat-trick in a 3-3 draw away to Dynamo Kyiv, then we played in Tbilisi against Krylya Sovetov. Edik always played well in Tbilisi, where he could feel the love from the fans. That day we were drawing 1-1 when he picked up the ball wide on the right, charged forward to the goalline then suddenly turned infield. From no angle just inside the box he lashed a swerving shot into the top corner. It was stunning, the sort of goal nobody had any right to score. You could hear a gasp before the roar from the Georgian supporters.

But with Edik in those days, nothing was ever straightforward. Aleksandr Medakin gave away a penalty with a handball and as the game began to slip away from us, you could see Edik getting more and more frustrated. A decision went against him and he began raging at the referee, Piotr Gavrilov from Sochi. Immediately you felt the fear: if he was sent off there would be no defending him. He was on probation and this would be the end of his World Cup and possibly worse. Thankfully Kuzma got involved as well, got between Edik and Gavrilov and so it was he who was set off. He always said he was just angry, but I think we all wondered if he had sacrificed himself for Edik.

That meant Kuzma was suspended for the game against Dinamo Tbilisi, so Gennadi Gusarov, at the time a promising 20 year old, moved inside and Vitali Arbutov took his place on the left wing. We'd beaten Dinamo 6-1 six months previously in the Cup, so everybody feared a backlash but we beat them 6-1 again. With Kuzma suspended, Edik was named as captain. He scored the second but he also set up four goals for Gusarov. By the end, the Georgians were on their feet applauding. It was one of those days when you could imagine everything was right with the world, maybe the last great day. Six weeks later, and for years after that, we looked back on that afternoon with great fondness and sadness.

After seven games of the season Torpedo were second, a point behind Spartak. Our last game before the championship broke for the World Cup was against Spartak at the Luzhniki. There were 105,000 there on a mild, cloudy Friday afternoon for a game that, even without what happened next, would have been remembered for a long time. Yes, neither goalkeeper covered themselves in glory, but the drama, the attacking play... it was a great game.

Anatoly Ilyin, part of the Olympic side, scored twice to put Spartak 2-0 up. But a minute after the second, Falin was fouled and Kuzma scored the penalty. Two minutes after that, he equalised, knocking in the rebound from a Falin shot: three goals in four minutes just before half-time. Ilyin completed his hat-trick just before the hour, but then, with seventeen minutes to go, Edik got the ball just inside the Spartak half. It was one of those classic Edik surges, the crowd rising as defenders fell away from him. And then, quite suddenly, bang! Before poor Valentin Ivakin had moved it was in the net. People blamed him for it, but only because they didn't understand Edik's genius. Other players had to set themselves for a shot, so keepers knew when it was coming. For him it was just a fluid movement as he ran. Edik hit it early, from outside the box, and Ivakin wasn't set. It wasn't his greatest goal. Maybe it wasn't even a great goal. But it was a typical goal. And perhaps that was the best thing we could have been given to remember him by over the seven years that followed.

....

The preparations for the World Cup began with a "Moscow XI" – the USSR national side in all but name – against East Germany. Edik scored three of our four goals. Then there was a proper international against England, the first time the sides had ever met. For that reason it should have been an occasion, but it was all a little flat – maybe because we knew we'd be facing them in Sweden the following month. I went to the game at Luzhniki. England had Bobby Robson, who would become their manager, playing in midfield and Tom Finney on the wing, but neither team played well. Kuzma equalised with twelve minutes to go and it finished 1-1.

Six days later, on 24 May, there was a game against Poland that didn't have official status. There was the usual banquet after, and Edik left the Leningradskaya Hotel with the factory bosses – a way of making sure he didn't get himself into trouble. And he did go home, but only after ringing a woman who told him it was too late for them to meet up.

Did we know about it at the club at the time? I honestly can't remember. Maybe we did, maybe we just heard after the investigation. Edik had so many women it was difficult to keep track. This one liked football. She'd got Edik's number somehow and rung him maybe six months earlier, during that period when it seemed he was getting into trouble every week. She was a university graduate who had married another student, had a child with him and then divorced. She worked in a bookshop. For a few weeks they telephoned each other and then she turned up after training one day to meet him in person. I think their first date was in Gorky Park, walking along the avenues like any other young couple. He went to her place a couple of times and then he took her on what you might call a public date, to watch Lokomotiv play the national second XI.

But, anyway, they didn't meet up that night. If they had, perhaps it would all have been different. You see now the fatal timeline, all the pieces falling into place. After the banquet Boris Tatushin, who had played in the Olympic team with Edik, spent the night with his girl, Inna, at the apartment of his friend Eduard Karakhanov, who was a pilot just back from service in the East. The next day, the players went to the tailor on Prospekt Mira to have their World Cup suits fitted. Afterwards a few players decided to go out.

They agreed to meet that afternoon by Russkiye Vina on Ulitsa Gor'kogo. The Spartak players were late and Edik, feeling weary, decided to go home, back to Avtozavodskaya. He was, he later told us, on his way to hail a cab when he saw Sergei Salnikov from Spartak reach the door of the wine shop. Salnikov, who was a senior player by then and knew Edik from the Olympic squad, offered to buy him a drink. It was a hot day. What was the harm in a refreshing dry white wine? So Edik accepted. They drank a glass each and were about to leave when Misha Ogonkov, Tatushin and Karakhanov turned up. Salnikov went home. Edik did not.

....

The first I knew was a hammering on the door. I was washing the plate from lunch in the sink – bread, a little herring and an onion, I recall; it's strange the details that stick. I'd been reading the newspaper and had fallen asleep in the chair, so it was probably mid-afternoon, later even. I could tell even from the knock that this was Misha and something terrible had happened. I remember clearly drying my hands and walking deliberately to the door, still holding the towel.

'He's done it this time,' Misha said. 'He's finished.'

'Edik?'

'Of course.'

I'd heard this from him before. Misha always exaggerated, always expected the worst. But I was also aware that Edik had been teetering on the cliff edge for a long, long time. I changed quickly while Misha paced about, swearing. We rushed to the club. There were discussions going on with the bosses from the factory and the union and the Party. Misha, in his role as liaison, had a function in that. I was there really as moral support. But I was also there because Misha knew I would want to be there, that I would want to know what was happening and help out however I could.

Certain moments remain in my mind with absolute clarity. I was standing by the samovar when Misha came back into the office, looked at Vera and then looked at me, and said the word 'rape'. That was the moment I knew this wasn't just another of Edik's scrapes and misadventures, that this was something far more serious. But the sequence of events, when I knew what, what I heard when? That is a blur.

There were those who said they couldn't believe it, that it wasn't like him. Fans whispered that he'd been set up, that this was the revenge of the authorities, or the big clubs getting their own back, that somebody – Yekaterina Furtseva, perhaps? – had it in for him. I wanted to believe that, and I thought of Narignani's denunciation, but in truth I could believe it of him only too well even if I tried not to admit that to myself. Not of course that I said anything; we just got on with the job of trying to get him out so he could play in the World Cup, or at least finish the league season with us.

Many years later, I got talking to Kuzma and he told me what he remembered. The players had met at the Yaroslavl station to take the train out to Tarasovka – which was Spartak's training camp but it was where the Soviet national team had based themselves. Edik was hungover and there were scratches on his face that he'd tried to cover up with powder. The national team doctor, Belakovsky, was angry with Edik for turning up in that state when they were supposed to be training for the World Cup, and then, giving him a quick once over on the train, he drew attention to bitemarks on Edik's finger. Lev Yashin, who was sitting near him, made a joke about the cat Edik had been playing with the night before. When they got to Tarasovka, Edik went for a nap, and then he and Lev Ivanovich went fishing – you know how Yashin loved to fish. By the time they got back to the base, the police had arrived.

The squad had been told to report to the Dinamo Stadium at 4.30pm the previous day, but Edik, Ogonkov and Tatushin had asked to be excused. One of the suits from the Sports Ministry noticed they were missing but Vladimir Moshkarkin, the great Torpedo striker who was working as general manager for the national team, had covered for them, for which he was later sacked.

After a couple of drinks at Russkiye Vina, the three players had decided they would leave the heat of Moscow and spend the day at the Tishkovsky reservoir – a last day of freedom before the hard work and discipline of the World Cup. Tatushin's girlfriend Inna joined them, and so did his pilot friend Karakhanov and his girlfriend Irina. Inna promised Edik and Ogonkov that girls would be found for them as well – that's how it was with footballers. Marina Lebedeva was planting potatoes when her friend Inna, Tatushin's girl, came to invite her. She was nineteen. She washed her hands and feet at the pump, and was still combing her hair and picking the dirt from under her nails on the way to meet the players. Or that's what they said later, maybe to make her seem purer. Inna also found a girl for Ogonkov, Tamara, whose father had read Narignani's attack on Edik. He warned his daughter to be careful and not to go with footballers but she ignored him.

You can imagine the scene. They laid out a rug on the grass in a clearing by the reservoir. There was champagne, cognac, vodka, beer and wine, stuffed peppers, apples, oranges and pickles. The players were anxious. They'd lied to Kachalin, claiming they were at a birthday party; they knew they had to behave. A group of lads recognised them, shouted to them, asked them if they wanted a game. The players drank quickly, hoping for the relaxation that alcohol provides. They kicked a football about with the girls.

Then Streltsov took Inna for a ride in Ogonkov's car. Streltsov had recently crashed his car and Ogonkov was worried he would crash his as well. And Tatushin began to get jealous and wonder about Inna and Streltsov. So Tatushin, Ogonkov, Tamara and Marina went off in the other car to try to find them. They couldn't but when they got back to the clearing Streltsov and Inna were already there.

They drank some more and then, at about 6.30, they decided to head for Karakhanov's parents' dacha. Ogonkov was driving. Tamara sat next to him. Karakhanov and his girl were on the back seat with Edik next to them. Marina sat on Edik's lap. He held her – one hand on her waist, the other on her head so she wouldn't bang it on the roof of the car. We know this from the trial, but I've thought about what happened a lot, tried to piece it together, to picture the scene. Edik kissed her on the back of the neck and then the cheek and tried to kiss her on the lips, but she wouldn't let him.

It's difficult. There is what happened, what they said happened in court, what they said happened privately and what I imagine happening. There's also what I hoped had happened: could it be this was not what it seemed, that it was a stitch-up? This long after, I'm afraid the strands have become tangled in my head. Who can say what the atmosphere was? Who can say who felt what or why? Who knows what signals were given, deliberately or unconsciously? Who knows how these were interpreted? Was Marina teasing Edik, or was she really denying him? We know now she was a virgin. Edik was experienced. Did he just think that she would give herself to him as so many had before?

Details emerged and people painted their pictures from them. All we can say is that the mood was fraught. Karakhanov tore Irina's blouse. He may have struck her. Ogonkov's shirt also got torn somehow and had to be stitched up by Tamara and Marina. The string of Tamara's necklace was accidentally broken by Ogonkov, spilling the beads across the floor. Tatushin's fear that Streltsov was moving in on Inna was a constant undercurrent, as was Karakhanov's that his Irina was really interested in Ogonkov.

I don't know. This was never my scene, the easy pick-ups footballers become accustomed to. I never understood where the lines were, and perhaps they didn't either. It all seems so messy, so sordid, but I suppose that happens with drink. Small doubts and irritations are magnified and would be forgotten with sobriety. Insignificant wrinkles become great mountains when scrutinised the following day. And if everybody in a closed environment were happy with their partner, if there were no such thing as jealousy, half the novels and plays and songs in the world would never have been written.

Marina and Tamara, it seems, although nobody was too clear, decided to go home and so they walked to the station. But they had no money for the train and Karakhanov and Edik drove after them in the car. They took them back to the dacha. They played table tennis. Karakhanov's parents, who owned the dacha, served them canned fish and cucumbers, then fried some cutlets for dinner. Marina and Tamara decided it was best to stay that night but to go back early the following day when the players had to drive into Moscow to join up with the squad. Again, who knows what the players thought that meant?

It got to nearly midnight. It was getting cool. Marina put on Edik's jacket. Karakhanov's parents went to sleep. Edik asked Marina to go to bed with him. She refused but he vowed she would be his. Again, without tone, without context, it's impossible to know if that were a threat or a clumsy joke intended to be charming. Edik made promises of marriage, said that Marina should come to Tarasovka to visit him. He kissed her, and she placed her hands on his chest to hold him back.

He was drunk. He pushed her out on to the terrace, which led to a room where Inna was standing. Marina saw her and felt less concerned. But she realised Inna did not look her in the eye.

So much we know. On this, all the witnesses, all the reports, everything that came out at the trial roughly agrees. I have played it in my mind over and over. Of what happened next, we have only fragments.

We know Marina bit Edik's finger. He said she began to scream and he placed his hand across her mouth to stop her waking the household. Did he hit her, or did he catch her accidentally when withdrawing his hand in pain? She scratched him, that is certain. There are those who are determined to believe Edik innocent who would dismiss all this. It is obvious there were flaws in how the investigation was conducted, that it set out to find him guilty. But even those minded to give him the benefit of the doubt, I think, must acknowledge at the very least that Edik behaved aggressively and that Marina was genuinely frightened.

Ogonkov and Tamara were in the car. They heard Marina scream. Tamara wanted to go to her aid, but Ogonkov stopped her, saying it was Karakhanov's property and he was closer.

What other details can we find? Irina said that when she left the room, Edik and Marina were asleep in each other's arms. Edik remembered nothing after the bite, just falling into a deep sleep. At some point that night, Marina ceased to be a virgin.

She woke to find her clothes hanging neatly by the bed. She fled home, distressed, her face badly bruised by Edik's hand. Could it really have been an accident, that blow? Perhaps. But however much I wanted to believe that, it feels unlikely. The most sympathetic explanation I can find is that, drunk, he overreacted and didn't know his own strength. But that is no defence. Marina, strangely, had no recollection of exactly how she came by her bruises.

By the morning, Tatushin and Inna had gone, as had Marina. Irina had left Karakhanov and slept in the car with Ogonkov and Tamara, and Karakhanov had ended up sleeping in the same room as Edik. Marina remembered in the night Edik asking him for a cigarette and a glass of water.

That scene is less easy to imagine than what happened the following day. The sunlight, the bleary eyes, the heavy heads, the attempts to piece together what had happened the previous evening. Edik got one of the girls to powder his face to try to hide the scratches, and they prepared for their return to the city.

Those details have struck many as strange. Could it be that, rejected by Irina, it was Karakhanov who raped Marina? He had the same blood type as Edik. The science couldn't tell us any more than that. Forensics then were not as they are now. I don't know. It is possible. Or perhaps there was consensual sex between Edik and Marina and Karakhanov, his lust unsated by Irina, then took advantage of their drunken sleep. These would be convenient excuses for those who want to find them. And I think an investigation less determined to find Edik guilty might have turned up more that would have proved things one way or the other.

But this talk troubles me. It troubled me then and it troubles me more now. Marina is always forgotten, the victim, the naïve girl who found herself in a situation far beyond her control. I can say the Edik for whom I had such admiration did not seem like a rapist, and that would be true. But in that 18 months from the Olympics to that night, he was increasingly not the Edik I had known and came to know again. In drink he could be wild. Even if Karakhanov was the villain, Edik behaved extremely badly that night.

Marina's parents persuaded her to go to the police and make a statement accusing Edik of rape. They also got Tamara to accuse Ogonkov.

That all emerged over the weeks, months, years that followed. I realise now, looking back at what I have written, that is not how I felt at the time when I was desperate for him to be innocent while fearing the worst. This is how I have come to feel, through thinking about and discussing it.

But when Misha banged on my door, all that was known was that Edik had been accused of rape. It was harder for Misha, of course. He had a terrible job, really, running around from one department to another, from the club to the factory to the Party, trying to co-ordinate a response. I was there really to help him. To make some phone calls, to find documents, to try to stay calm amid the panic.

The first two days, Edik and Ogonkov were held in the prosecutor's office in Mytishchi, to the north of Moscow. They slept on chairs there and were given tea. Tatushin took them bread and sausage. At that stage, both players were still denying even having had sex with their accusers. Finally at lunchtime on May 28, Edik was formally committed for trial and taken to a cell down in the basement. Two days later he was taken to the Butyrki detention centre. Up till then, I think there'd still been some hope Edik might get out and be available for the first World Cup game, against England in Gothenburg on July 8. We knew it was serious, but I don't think at first any of us realised how serious. We were still treating it as a football problem. What games would he miss, how long would he be suspended for, that kind of thing. I don't think what the possible consequences of a trial may be really occurred to any of us, even Misha.

It all becomes blurred, the order of events, who said what when. When it became apparent that Karakhanov and Edik shared a blood type, that offered a way out, although it would have meant a lieutenant in the air force taking the blame. But it seemed to us that was never even looked into, neither as a way of getting Edik off the hook, nor as what might actually have happened.

I know there are those who think Karakhanov was an agent of the state, that he skilfully lured Edik into a trap. But if that were true, it was a very well-hidden plan. Would he really have risked getting as drunk as he seemingly did? Would he have been cunning enough to row with Irina? If he had been working for the KGB, would *Konsomolskaya Pravda* really have described him, as it later did, as somebody who had received his officer's rank 'by some misunderstanding'?

And then there is the question of who. Who would have ordered this? It's one thing to think that the authorities lost patience with Edik and decided after another outrage to act, quite another to imagine somebody plotted against him, not just before the World Cup.

Tatushin, it should be said, did everything he could for Edik. He didn't just take him food. Inna, Tatushin's girlfriend, had known Marina since school and knew the parents. Tastushin took Sofia Frolovna to visit them. She took gifts – jam, sausages, apples, marshmallows – and promised Edik would marry their daughter (although, technically, Alla was still his wife).

She begged for forgiveness. She was a mother contemplating her son going to prison. They all sobbed together. Tamara was persuaded to write to the Prosecutor of the Mytishchi district withdrawing her accusation. Marina scribbled something similar although less formal, saying she forgave Edik.

Edik did almost nothing for himself. Misha was furious with him. 'He just stands there,' I remember him saying, 'like it's a hot day in Kuibyshev and he can't be bothered to run. He's just waiting for us to sort it out for him.' Part of that, of course, was the pressure Misha was under, and Misha always tended to rage at people first (when they weren't present; one of the reasons he had his job was that he was impeccably polite in person) and calm down later, but I recognised the Edik he was describing. I could imagine him, resenting the questions, responding petulantly, making the situation worse. He was a child of twenty.

But even as I say that, I find myself caught in the contradictions. Imagine I hadn't known Edik. Imagine all I knew of him was what I'd read in *Konsomolskaya Pravda*. Imagine I'd known Marina for four or five years. What then would I want to happen? Would I have sympathy for the professional athlete who'd brutalised her? Would I care he was immature? Of course not. Ah, his defenders say, but maybe it wasn't him. And maybe it wasn't. But he was the one with scratches on his face. And he was the one whose hand had left bruises on her cheek. And he was the one she accused. And he was the one who, I fear, unused to having his desires thwarted, might have forced himself upon her. And he was the one who seemed indifferent to defending himself. Misha, I know, although he never said as much, thought he had done it. But then Misha lived with Eva and Eva, not unreasonably, had strong views on this sort of thing.

And I think as well Edik was unable to believe that he would not get away with this, as he had got away with so much before. He was the great Streltsov. He *was* a star. Somebody would stop the train so he could catch up. That was how it had been for him for five years; why should that not be the case here? I don't know. I don't know. Maybe on some level he acknowledged his guilt and accepted his punishment. But what I think, what Misha thought, is that he was bored, that he spent the interrogations and the trial waiting for it to be over so he could go and play football and drink again.

I heard from Vera that soon after Edik had been moved to Butyrki, Alla had gone with a schoolfriend to visit him, taking the baby and a bag of nappies with her. She went in, leaving her friend in the car, and explained who she was to an old and fat policeman. He just told her she was better off without her husband. At that, she turned and left, and told her friend she was never going back. Alla asked if she could have the car, but Edik instead gave it to his mother. Perhaps he just reasoned that Sofia Frolovna would fight harder to get him out of there, or maybe that just tells you all you need to know about his relationships with the two women in his life at that time. Alla filed for divorce soon after.

....

The World Cup began on June 8. I listened to our game against England in my apartment. It was the evening and I couldn't have borne company. Edik was still in jail, still awaiting trial. Nikita Simonyan scored early and we got a second about ten minutes after half-time, but England came back and equalised with a penalty from Finney with five minutes to go. We beat Austria in the second game – Kuzma got our second in a 2-0 win – but then we lost to that really strong Brazil side, which meant a play-off against England who had drawn all their games. We won, 1-0, with a goal midway through the second half from Anatoly Ilyin but I struggled to take much pleasure in it. All I could think was how much better it would have been if Edik had been there. But he wasn't, and Igor Netto wasn't fully fit so only played in one match, and we ended up going out a little limply in the quarter-final against Sweden. That was June 19, and still nothing had really happened with Edik. He was still at Butyrki.

By the time the trial began, Brazil had won the World Cup and a seventeen year old called Pelé had emerged as the brightest talent on the planet. Which of us who had watched Edik over the previous four years did not wonder whether we could have won the World Cup and everybody might have been celebrating a twenty year old called Streltsov? But he was in the Butyrki detention centre because he couldn't control himself when alcohol was available and that led him to do stupid things and perhaps a terrible thing.

The trial was held in secret. Ogonkov and Tatushin were called as witnesses. Andrey Starostin was allowed to attend so we heard from him what was going on. At the time, I think we largely accepted what he told us – or rather, what he told Misha and Misha told me. But as time has gone by, I wonder how reliable he was. He had had his own problems, of course, being sent to the camps in 1942 and claiming it was because he played for Spartak and his whole family were hated by Beria, when we all knew it was because they'd been fiddling ration cards. So maybe he was inclined to believe the footballer and distrust the court, I don't know.

And Andrey Petrovich was no fan of Marina Lebedeva. He said she flirted with the court, acted like a heroine and then dropped hints that she and Streltsov were somehow still together. I think a lot of people wondered what she thought was going to happen if she went to a dacha with a load of footballers – as though a nineteen year old couldn't be naïve and confused, caught up in things far beyond her control or understanding. Even Edik's lawyer accused her of being "too frivolous". At some point she withdrew her statement of forgiveness and reasserted the initial complaint, which Misha took as evidence that the prosecutor was pressuring her.

The newspapers stepped up their attack. They demanded the harshest penalties. They echoed Narignani's assault. Edik thought himself too grand for normal society. When his team-mates took the bus, he was driven in limousines. He drank only the finest cognac. It was all nonsense. If he drank fine cognac it was because he learned to drink at the banquets they forced him to attend. All the praise he received as a sportsman caused him to lose any sense of responsibility or morality. Honoured too young with awards and a nice apartment, he judged himself only by his sporting success. All of it was true and none of it was true. Certainly none of it was fair.

And so the rumours spread that Edik was being scapegoated, that he was a poppy grown too tall. They feared he would defect in Sweden, they said, which was absurd. That's the problem with these closed trials. When the public cannot hear the evidence, conspiracy takes root. It was Furtseva! It was Dinamo! It was Khrushchev himself! Far easier to believe that than to accept a stupid boy had done a series of stupid things and paid an awful price.

The facts of the trial were these: Edik was charged on two counts, of hooliganism and rape. He denied the hooliganism and admitted the rape. His lawyer asked for a sentence of five years. Of course none of that means anything. Who knows what pressure was applied, what promises were made. Misha very early accepted there was nothing more he or the club would do. It had gone beyond them. I remember him that summer, listening to the World Cup on the radio, drinking heavily, his usual energy gone. In court, Edik apologised to Marina, remained stoical. There were rumours he had insulted the judge or said he should have stayed in France when he had the opportunity, but none of it was true. He was dignified or numb, whichever version you prefer. And he admitted being a rapist. He was sentenced to twelve years' hard labour.

At the beginning of August, Edik sent a postcard to his mother. Dr Yegorov saw it. It took a tone of cheery practicality, noting that the supreme court had approved the sentence and that he would be sent to the camp soon. He told her to look after herself and not worry about him, to sell the car if she needed to. He said his shoes were leaking and asked her to bring him an old sweater, warm socks and an Astrakhan hat, and to buy some new boots and nail horseshoes onto the soles so they didn't wear through.

Глава первая

1963

─────────────────────── **TORPEDO** ───────────────────────

Soviet League: *P38 W12 D16 L10 F46 A41 Pts40.* **Final position:** *12th of 20.*
Soviet Cup: *Lost in third round to Shakhtar Donetsk.*

It was a damp, grey day in autumn. The birches had turned and the pavements were slick with fallen leaves. Torpedo had fallen away after the World Cup, the heart ripped out of everybody. There were still a handful of games remaining but we ended up seventh. I'd been invited to Misha's flat for dinner.

Even before the trial, I hadn't seen him as much socially as I once had. There'd been a time as well when I'd hoped there might be more to Eva's niceness than mere friendliness, when I met her occasionally out of the office, but after they married and had children, I didn't see them so much. This was the first time I'd been to their place in months.

We were all worn down by then. There was physical exhaustion towards the end of the season, particularly after the stress of the trial, but there was also an emotional fatigue, this player we'd all known for years, invested so much in emotionally, sent off to the gulag. The kids went to bed after dinner and we were working our way through a bottle of brandy I'd brought when Misha revealed that there'd been another postcard from Edik to his mother. Dr Yegorov, poor man, felt a sense of responsibility to her so he was still going over to see her every couple of weeks and she'd shown it to him.

I remember quite clearly the rush of excitement I felt. Edik could still contact us, despite everything. They'd tried, clumsily, to write him out of history. The goals he'd scored in 1958 were erased from the record. Who scored when we beat Chisninau Moldova 3-1? There were two for Yuri Falin and "another scorer". Who got the equaliser against Spartak? A blank space. It was ludicrous. He became a non-person, but he still existed.

He'd been moved from Butyrki to a transfer facility and had written from there, insisting he was fine and asking for boots, a padded work jacket, a shaving brush, a red woollen T-shirt and a belt for his trousers. Again he urged his mother to sell whatever she needed to and to look after herself.

I have a clear picture in my head of that night, sitting against the wooden panelling in their kitchen, the bottle half-empty on the table, our three glasses, smeared with fingerprints, the ashtray full, the air blue with smoke. Eva sat near the stove, her hair duller than it had been in her youth and the lines from her nose to the side of her mouth clear, but her eyes still sparkled with life and she still had the same throaty chuckle.

Once Edik had been mentioned, of course we spoke of nothing else. We had no idea how to interpret this latest message, no idea the extent to which it had been censored, either by Edik or the authorities. I wondered whether the positive tone, looking out for his mother, was a sign of growing maturity, but Eva thought that if anything it was probably a sign he hadn't quite grasped the seriousness of the situation.

In retrospect, I think she was right, but then she had always understood people. Certainly she understood Edik better than the rest of us. I think it was her, more than anybody, who made me accept that Edik might be guilty. Others made their excuses for him; she was clear he'd been running wild for too long and that whatever had actually happened at the dacha that night, his behaviour towards Marina – and women in general – had been reprehensible.

After that we met up probably once a month, usually at their place because it was bigger and because of the kids, very occasionally at mine. Always, we ended up talking about Edik and Dr Yegorov's latest information from Sofia Frolovna. Initially Edik seemed almost to relish being assigned to a logging camp, not really understanding what it meant and thinking his physical strength would make it bearable. I wondered as well whether he was looking to punish himself, whether that was his acknowledgement of his wrongdoing but I think in that first year, he believed it was just a matter of time before he would be released, that the sentence somehow would be commuted by somebody.

The reality soon became apparent. In the first few weeks at the camp, he slapped a young inmate who had been bothering him. I never fully understood the details, but apparently that was against the code, so they beat him – and beat him quite badly. He was left with broken ribs. But we only found out about that much later, after he'd recovered, when it was far too late for us to worry. After that, they left him alone. Again I don't know why, but the story was he was protected by some criminal elements he'd met in prison in Moscow.

And Edik was bitter. He felt let down by the club and, particularly, by the bosses. Senyukov, Velokanov and Yemishev sent him a package on behalf of the team and he told his mother he would have rejected it if he could have. He didn't want our charity. I think he was worried as well about whether the club was really looking after his mother as well as it could. In that, maybe he had a point. But I don't know whether he was equally concerned for Alla. Vera was never in such regular contact with her after the divorce. And whenever I heard the arguments about how badly Edik was treated, I kept coming back to the same thought: he had had warning after warning and then he did something terrible.

....

Edik was sent initially to a transfer camp at Kirov, and then on to Vyatlag to start logging. Almost as soon as he got there he sent a telegram to his mother begging for a food parcel. The work was hard, loading and chopping wood, and when he got back to the barracks there was nothing to do, other than a film screened in the dining-room once a week. Not that it mattered: he was so tired, he told his mother, that it felt like his hands would drop off and all he wanted to do was sleep.

But food was always his main concern. He granted his mother power of attorney to sell the car so she could afford to send him food each month – and told her to send any type of food she could because there was nothing edible there. As autumn drew on he asked for warmer clothes, and he asked specifically for the shaving kit he had been given following that game in Hanover.

After a while Edik was moved to another camp. He worked from eight in the morning to five in the afternoon, then was able to study. An old convict helped him find lighter work as a technician at a power plant which didn't just make his life a little easier but also I think suggested to Edik and to everybody else that there might be some hope. The authorities could have insisted on him performing the hardest labour and the fact they didn't suggested that despite everything he still had some friends working for him in Moscow.

Sofia Frolovna didn't sell the car for a long time. She got into debt, had more and more health problems, and would complain a lot to Dr Yegorov, the usual stuff about how she didn't want to live any more. I think she was hoping the club would bail her out, but Dr Yegorov had to be firm in the end – and I think Edik was too in his letters – and she sold the car. She sent Edik some money but only after he had instructed her how to hide it in a box of sugar so it wouldn't get stolen.

They kicked Sofia Frolovna out of the apartment. She made a big fuss about that, but what did she expect? There was no justification for one woman living in a big two-room apartment like that.

In his second year in the gulag, Edik asked Sofia Frolovna to send him a ball. They'd set up a league between the various camps. It was supposed to be for full-time employees, but it was decided that they could field three "variable staff", as they put it, as well. So once a week, Edik played for the camp team in the Vyatlag Cup. It was clear from his letters what a release that was for Edik, even playing in intense heat amid clouds of midges and mosquitoes. Just being able to leave his camp to go and play at other camps made life a little easier. And of course his team won the tournament, even though Edik had to stop playing for a while after he strained a muscle in his leg. There was also a time when he fell and broke a bone in his hand, so he had to dictate the letters for another prisoner to write.

It was around that time that a new code was introduced that effectively meant that prisoners, so long as they behaved themselves, would only have to serve half their sentence. There was some thought he could be out as early as November 1961. That too did a lot to lift Edik's mood. He quit smoking. He started reading books. He asked his mother to get Galya to send him a fixture list for the Soviet championship. It was as though he was beginning to take an interest in things again, that the numbness that had fallen over him when he was arrested had been lifted and his bitterness towards the club was beginning to dissipate.

....

From Torpedo's point of view, that was a good year to take an interest. We'd climbed to fifth in 1959, but 1960 was something else, for all he subsequently did in Kyiv, I would say Viktor Maslov's greatest achievement.

That was the first year of the sub-groups, a baffling format by which the league was split into two groups of 11. You played everybody in your group twice and then there were four mini-leagues to decide the final positions. So the first job was to finish in the top three. We started well and never looked back. At some point that year, I stopped missing Edik and started watching the team for what it was.

Kuzma scored in three of the first four games and played consistently well for the first time since Edik had been arrested – although in truth their relationship had begun to fray from the Olympics onwards. Some said Edik blamed Kuzma for him missing the final, but I think the issue was the other way: Kuzma became frustrated by the way Edik went off the rails. Yuri Falin was excellent that year. Slava Metreveli, the little Georgian winger we got from Torpedo Gorky in 1958, had maybe his best season – and would score for the national side in the final of the inaugural European Championship as we beat Yugoslavia. But in a year in which all the front four were brilliant, Gennady Gusarov stood out. We didn't lose until the tenth game of the season, in June, and we only dropped ten points in total in the twenty group games. We finished six points clear at the top, comfortably qualifying for championship play-off.

You have to bear in mind what an amazing thing this was for us. Torpedo had never won the league. There was an expectation that under pressure we would blow it. But Viktor Aleksandrovich kept everybody grounded. Dinamo Moscow and Dynamo Kyiv looked to be our two biggest rivals but we beat both of them within the first four games and Gusarov scored a hat-trick against CSKA. We lost at Lokomotiv but when Gusarov got a late equaliser in Rostov against SKA it meant we could seal the championship in Kyiv in the penultimate game.

We all met at the club to listen to the game on the radio. It was like the Olympics again except this time we knew there was champagne waiting.

Slava Metreveli gave us the lead after three minutes from Kuzma's cross but Viktor Serebryanikov equalised 10 minutes later. They had a goal ruled out for offside just before half-time then, 11 minutes into the second half, Nikolai Manoshin, who was only 20, dribbled past two men and crossed for Gusarov to put us 2-1 up. That final 34 minutes were agony. On the radio it seemed like attack after attack from Lobanovskyi, Serebryanikov, Bazilevich... We paced about. We went outside. We drank tea. We drank vodka. We talked. We smoked silently. Eva was there with a black-and-white ribbon in her hair and there was a little crease of concern above her nose every time Dynamo advanced. But we held on and the title was ours. Two years after our best player had gone to the gulag, both Torpedo and the USSR had won trophies. Could I bring myself to believe that they were right when they said this proved individuality was counter-productive in football? I could not. But perhaps the turmoil of 1958 had made the club stronger. And perhaps without Edik, Gena Gusarov and Slava Metreveli had space to breathe.

I don't know when Edik found out we'd won the league, but it was around then that his football in the camp stopped. He was moved from Vyatlag and the new camp had no league. Sofia Frolovna, who turned 50 that year, still made sure he had a ball, but he was just kicking it about after that, not playing in any kind of competition.

Torpedo finished top of the sub-group in 1961 as well. We really were a very good side in those days and Gena Gusarov was top-scorer in the league that season with 22. They'd changed the system again so that in the second phase you played only the teams from the other sub-group then added the points gained in the second phase to those gained in the first. That effectively gave us a four-point head start, but we didn't take advantage and ran out of steam badly. We twice lost to Spartak Moscow, and took only a point from Spartak Yerevan and Dynamo Kyiv, who ended up champions, four points clear of us. Maslov left after that, went to Rostov-na-Donu for reasons that never seemed to make much sense, and with him went the guiding force of that team.

Edik started to get frustrated again. There were petitions and official letters from the club and factory workers' organisations but it became apparent that they weren't going to let him out that winter. He went back to studying – he was doing the eighth grade then, but he admitted it was tough after a long break and his tone suggested he was finding it tiresome. There were the requests for clothes and another ball. At one point the guards even paid for a ball that Edik managed to get delivered.

Dr Yegorov also told us that Edik was including in his letters to his mother letters to Galya, who was clearly more than just a neighbour. Had she become some kind of long-distance girlfriend? It was hard to know, although he wrote of his "feelings" for her and how they would have to talk when he was released. Maybe it was just that she was more sensible and reliable than Sofia Frolovna, although Eva had a theory that he liked the idea of having a wife waiting for him, that it made him feel less alone.

A Comrade Rubichev was put in charge of Edik's case. Sofia Frolovna begged Edik to write to him, but he refused. His excuse was that if he'd been in his teens it would have been reasonable to beg for mercy, but he was 25 – 25! Those lost years! – and so it would be meaningless. And he said he had no respect for writing. But it seemed to us he'd given up again, that he sought no happy future, that he couldn't face more rejection and was just waiting for deliverance. The bosses at ZIL made representations for him and eventually it became clear he would be released in 1963, after serving two thirds of his sentence. They tried to present that as clemency, but Misha, who understood these things, said that with the law as it stood they couldn't keep him any longer.

Even at that time, though, Edik was clearly following the fortunes of Torpedo. Things began to fall apart in 1962. We finished fourth in the subgroup to at least have the chance of competing for the championship but in truth we never came close and ended up seventh, ten points behind the champions Spartak. In December 1962 we went on a tour to Scotland and something went badly wrong. I stayed in Moscow so have only the rumours and whispers to go on but I think it's fair to say the boys discovered a taste for Scotch whisky. They beat Rangers, supposedly the strongest side, but then lost 4-3 to Kilmarnock and suffered a 6-0 humiliation against Heart of Midlothian. Edik wrote to his mother demanding to know what had gone wrong. Fans had sent him a postcard telling him that Sanya Medakin, Valery Voronin and Gena Gusarov were all leaving and begging him to write to them to persuade them to stay. I could see their point: nobody wants to see their heroes leave. But I also knew that the life of a club is more complicated than that. There are always reasons and I'd come to understand that sometimes players have to be moved on for the good of everybody. I don't know if Edik ever did write to them but Gusarov joined Dinamo that winter, Medakin stayed one more year and Voronin never left – although as it turned out, it might have been better for him if he had, wonderful midfielder though he was.

Edik worked as a turner for a while. The work was less physically demanding but because he was an apprentice he didn't get paid, so the requests to his mother and Galya became more regular. His attempt to give up smoking ended. Then they moved him again, to a camp in Elektrostal, which was much nearer Moscow. He worked there at a military factory, which was dangerous because they had no respirators in the paint shop or ear-protectors where the machinery was loud. For four months he ground metal with a sandblaster, which may be where he developed his lung condition, then the administration found him a much easier job as a librarian.

But it wasn't long before they moved him again, to Donskoye in the Tula region, where he worked at the 41st quartz mine near the Novomoskovsk factory. The labour there was brutal but the head of the local Department of the Ministry of Internal Affairs was a football fan and encouraged him to kick a ball around when his shift was over. He even practised 30 and 40m sprints – beginning to imagine the time when he would be released and he might be able to play properly again.

That was where he played the match they wrote about much later in *Komsomolskaya Pravda*, after the rehabilitation. Who knows what the truth of it was, or who had arranged what, but Edik was put on a team with some hopeless players while the opposition were convicts who were decent players and were quite happy to rough him up. At first, he kept out of harm's way, avoiding the penalty area and playing at half-pace. But as the goals flew into his side's net and the tackles rained in on him, he snapped and suddenly began to play properly, barging through challenges, brushing off his opponents on this rough Siberian pitch as he had once done in the finest stadiums in the country. His team came back into the game and the watching prisoners, about a thousand of them, began to roar their approval. It was so loud that a neighbouring village raised the alarm, thinking there must be a riot. But when the guards arrived, they found Edik being tossed in the air by celebrating prisoners.

Did it happen? I'm doubtful. Everything is too neat: him fighting back against the bullies, none of it rings true. Edik never, to my knowledge, spoke of it, so I think it's probably yet another myth, a story with some truth that has been exaggerated over the years. But that's what made him the legend he was, the sense that it might be true.

So perhaps at the 41st mine, things weren't too bad, but then he was moved to the 45th. They took Edik's ball away and banned him from training. He asked his mother to approach the ZIL director Alexey Krylov to intercede with Major-General Khlopkov on his behalf. I don't know if that made any difference, but he started doing exercises every morning to prepare himself for freedom. By December of 1962, he was counting down the days till his sentence was two-thirds served at the end of January. A friend of his from the camp, Gena, was released and stayed for a time with Sofia Frolovna, trying to get used to Moscow again.

Edik's application for parole was heard on February 4. Various statements were made that spoke positively of his character. His behaviour in the camps had been good, the only possible violation that incident in which he was beaten. The judge asked if he acknowledged his guilt and Edik said yes. The decision went in his favour. He was released.

Sofia Frolovna, the team administrator Georgy Kamensky and Viktor Shustikov went to collect him in a black Volga provided by the party manager of the ZIL central committee Arkady Volsky, who had previously run the foundry. I think Kamensky's appearance was significant: it showed the club still supported him and for Edik that probably meant a lot.

But he was not allowed to return to football straight away. How Torpedo would have liked to have had him back for that 1963 season after the chaos at the end of 1962. And how he desperately wanted to play. He had lost five years of a career that, at best, rarely last more than fifteen. And who knew what else he had lost in the camps: they are not exactly designed to encourage physical fitness. But what else could Edik do? It's true he had completed the ninth grade in the gulag, and that he had experience in certain factory jobs, but he had this one great skill. To deny him – and the USSR – that ability seemed absurd and cruel.

Edik kept himself to himself in those first weeks after his release. It was a long time before I saw him. Dr Yegorov said he looked tired, his boyish face prematurely aged, his hair gone: "our young hussar is no longer young" was the phrase he used. He had lost weight. He was glad to be out, but struggled with liberty, especially as it wasn't true liberty. But he didn't drink – which at least was something and perhaps showed his new seriousness. And he kept studying, doing lessons at the technical college to complete his tenth grade.

ZIL had to decide what to do with him, so they found him a job on a tiny salary in the tool shop. He settled to it quietly enough but what nobody seemed to have considered was that Alla by then had a job in the factory, working as a secretary for Anatoly Krieger, the great automobile designer.

Vera had stayed in touch with Alla, not often but enough to know what was going on. She had no contact with Edik until 1960, when Mila was two. Some lads from Perovo she'd never met before went to her apartment and asked to take photographs to send to Edik. She wrote to him after that. He replied, quickly, with a long letter, but with no great tenderness, no real questions about her or how she was getting on. The phrase that stood out, that Vera remembered, was 'how's your baby?' Not "our" baby but "your" baby, as though he had had nothing to do with her. Sofia Frolovna never visited her, never asked after her granddaughter until after Edik had been released.

Alla asked him what he would do when he was free, which was still a long way off at that point, and he was non-committal, and said he would have to wait and see what would happen. Which I suppose was fair enough, but it also confirmed to Alla what she'd already accepted, that there was nothing in their relationship to be salvaged. But then he sent her a letter from the prison at Kirovo-Chepetsk, and declared his love for her, asking if she wanted to cancel the divorce and get married again.

So it was complicated, or at least on Edik's side it was. With women he never knew his own mind. I think he loved the idea of being part of a family, and knew he had responsibilities, but when it came down to it, at least at that age, he chafed against the restrictions of marriage.

Alla told Mila who her father was, gave her pictures of him, told Vera how Mila would sit on her potty holding a picture clipped from a magazine in her hand, would keep saying, 'Daddy! Daddy!' I suppose she was soon old enough to know that other children had both a mother and a father and she had only one parent.

And then one day, Edik saw her across the factory. He admitted to Dr Yegorov that his heart skipped a beat, but then he quickly – too quickly, Dr Yegorov said – blurted out that she was seeing 'some clever Jew'. I don't know whether that was true. I don't know who he meant. But it was true that ZIL had a lot of Jewish designers, many of whom had been jailed by Stalin and then released, and it was also true that Alla was more than capable of flirting. But I don't know. What seemed more significant to me was that Edik appeared jealous.

Soon after that he finally made an effort to go and see his daughter. Alla's mother had taken Mila, who by then was five, so Alla could go out on a date. Alla was getting ready to leave when she saw a familiar hat and coat. He was with a woman she recognised, Zhenya Lavrishchev, and they had their mothers with them. They circled the apartment building, as though plucking up courage to visit. Then, out of breath from having walked up the stairs to the fourth floor, Zhenya's mother knocked on the door. Edik again had persuaded an older woman to have the difficult conversation for him.

Zhenya's mother asked Alla where Mila was and Alla decided to be difficult, as I think she probably had the right to be, and asked what she wanted.

'Oh, I'd like to see your girl. Sofia Frolovna is here, Edik is here…'

'What does that mean? She's not a doll! She's a child, a living person!' And then she said something brusque.

'Oh, you are rude,' Zhenya's mother said. 'I see now they were right about you.' And so Alla knew Edik, Sofia Frolovna, Zhenya and her mother had all been discussing her. She packed up and left and didn't return until late that evening.

It makes me uncomfortable, picking through the rubble of their relationship. I'm sure Viktor Maslov's view of her was rose-tinted, but equally Alla had a right here, surely, to be furious. Five years she'd brought up their child alone and then suddenly there was Edik sending his new girl's mother demanding to see her.

But anyway, Edik turned up a little later that day, by which time Alla's mother and Mila were home. The girl ran to him in tears and he hugged her, but there was no great reconciliation. Edik never went back to the apartment. Sofia Frolovna turned up at the kindergarten on Mila's birthday. But for the most part they kept out of her life.

Not long after that, Edik was introduced to Raisa who was, well, she was clearly what he needed. She was a larger lady, but he had always liked that, matronly even, she worked at the Central Store and she lived with her mother and sisters on the sixth floor of a block on Ulitsa Saikin, above a fish shop near the Avtozavodsky Bridge. Her father had died in 1958, a few weeks before the trial, and Edik seemed to fit in to the family as a sort of older brother or father figure. At first he hid Raisa from his mother, perhaps remembering the conflicts between Sofia Frolovna and Alla, but it quickly became apparent that this wasn't just one of his flings.

Maybe it was simply his age, or maybe the camps had changed him, maybe he'd been looking for this all along, but it also became apparent that one of the things Edik relished about this relationship was the family that came with it. We heard of a family celebration at which he had made a point of kissing every uncle and aunt, every cousin, as if they had known each other for years. And it wasn't as though Raisa's family was like that. I think they were probably a little embarrassed. And there was another time when he'd burned his backside on a heater in the Turkish baths and showed the scar, quite unabashed, to one of the aunts.

....

Torpedo had started that season badly. There were too many changes to the squad and we'd won only one of the first six games when Yuri Zolotov was sacked and Nikolai Morozov returned. And there was the issue of Edik, constant rumours that his career was over or that he was ready to come back. Nobody had a clue what was going on and he was happy enough at that stage just to keep his head down.

He studied in the faculty of engines and after a while the factory put him to work as a technician in quality control, where he was effectively back to doing what he'd done in the Fraser factory a decade earlier. Later, he got his professional driver's licence and would sit next to the actual driver during tests. Cars would be selected at random from the assembly line and taken outside Moscow to be tested on different surfaces.

People began to ask what a ban from football actually meant. Nobody seemed quite sure. They could stop him playing the league, but they couldn't stop him from playing altogether. After a while, he started playing for the workshop team in the Moscow league. Everybody was talking about it, but I felt uneasy. Given how diminished he would inevitably be, did I want to see him again? Was it wise? Should people from the club be going to watch? But I did, eventually. I couldn't stay away. I didn't tell Misha or Eva, didn't want to admit to anybody I was going to see him and so I stood alone, smoking anxiously and waiting for him to emerge.

Even forewarned by Dr Yegorov, I was shocked. His hair had always been of a type that would have thinned as he aged, but it was receding badly. And of course the youthful roundness of face, the slight pudginess he had, would never have lasted, but he was notably hard of face, creases scoring his brow and his cheeks. In five years he had aged fifteen. In the warm-up he slapped a shot over the bar like somebody from the accounts department who'd never played before, leaning back, body shape all wrong. It was horrible to see. But then in the game itself there was one sudden turn, sending a defender the wrong way, using the outside of his foot, checking back and the pushing off in the opposite direction that made you remember what he had been, the athleticism, the balance, the grace.

He said that the years in the camp had made him stronger, broader of shoulder, but he wasn't fit. He couldn't run, he couldn't sprint, and the specific muscles you use for kicking and the explosive pace that had been his trademark were gone. The more he played the more they began to push the boundaries. Nobody at the club knew what level he was allowed to play at. The ban was simultaneously absolute and entirely vague. He played a game for Torpedo's reserves against Dinamo reserves and, although he scored, he said that he felt ill. He just didn't have the stamina for even that level of football any more.

So he kept playing for the workshop team. The standard of that league was very good in those days and drew a lot of attention. Nikita Simonyan and Nikolai Dementiev from Spartak, having reached their late thirties, were playing for club sides, and so were the Mayorov and Starshinov brothers. Thousands would turn out to watch Edik play. He wasn't what he had been, of course, but there were glimmers of the old player and he was, of course, greeted rapturously by supporters. To them he was a returning hero. Nobody thought too much about why he was unable to play. I was uneasy because it seemed to me a provocation, but Eva was the only one I heard really express doubts on moral grounds. When a rapist has served his term should he be allowed to resume his life? I don't know, but nobody seemed even to be considering that. A lot of people still wanted to believe he was innocent.

And the more he played, the better he got, the more people began to wonder why he shouldn't play in the league. Torpedo began to push back against the ban. They started picking him for friendlies. And that was what led to the famous incident in Gorky, although that was technically a game between the two car plants: ZIL from Moscow and Volga from Gorky.

I was there for that one, working. I remember it clearly. There was a big crowd in the stadium, all there to see Edik, happy in the late afternoon sunshine. I was just making my way up from the dressing-room area to the stand with Misha when I saw one of those anonymous men in suits whose very anonymity makes clear who they are. He insisted he had to see the coach urgently. We both knew he wouldn't be happy. He hated being disturbed before games, took it very seriously even though it was only a works team, but Misha went to get him.

When Misha came up to the stand a few minutes later, he had that distant look with his lips tight that I'd come to know well. He shook his head slightly as he sat down. 'They're not letting him play,' he said, but he was already working out the next move, trying to work out the possibilities. Eventually he sighed and almost visibly relaxed. I took a swig from my hip-flask and held it out to him but it was almost as though he couldn't see it. 'This is it, how they react,' he said, gesturing around the bowl of the stadium. Then he pointed upwards. 'And how they react.'

That's why Misha was so much more successful than me. There were times when I could pretend to myself that it was my leg held me back but it wasn't. I mean, it didn't help, but Misha was just smarter than me. He saw the possibilities. It hadn't even occurred to me that the crowd might react in any way, or that it might be significant. Even then, I was a little baffled. What did he expect the crowd to do?

I found out soon enough. The teams trotted out onto the pitch to the customary applause. Attuned to it, you could almost hear them waiting for Edik, to give him a big roar, to welcome him back, and then the confusion and disappointment when they realised he wasn't there. Even worse was when Edik appeared in the stand. He didn't do anything. He just sat down. It could have been just that he'd picked up an injury, but word must have got round. Their fury was extraordinary. It began in one corner: a few people whistling and jeering, and then it got louder and louder and spread all around the stadium. I'd never heard anything like it. I'd never experienced anything like it. In those days you just didn't criticise the authorities like that.

It went on and on. The game started and still they were howling in anger. They stood up and stamped their feet on the benches and started to chant his name, 'Streltsov! Streltsov!' It was incredible. Edik sat motionless, I think a little terrified at the passions he could unleash, and this extraordinary situation. I assumed it would pass, but it didn't. It got louder and louder, wave after wave, like a great dam had broken. Then I saw the fire. At first I couldn't work out what was going on, flames shooting up, first in little pockets here and there and then a great mass, and I realised they'd rolled up newspapers to make torches and had lit them to create this display of their anger. All because a footballer – a convicted rapist, as Eva would always remind us – had not taken the field.

Misha went off to try to sort things out. He just stood up and went, murmuring, 'Sorry.' I wondered if I should follow him, but he hadn't asked for my help and by the time I'd thought about going after him, I'd realised that I wouldn't be able to keep up. One of the bosses of the Volga factory in Gorky, Misha told me later, told Arkady Volsky, the party leader at ZIL, that they had to bring Edik on in the second half, that if they didn't he was worried the stadium would be burned to the ground.

So Edik did come out for the second half and there was a great roar, like this was a vital goal in a Cup final. The atmosphere really was incredible, like nothing I'd ever experienced before. There was something very strange in the air that afternoon, an almost hysterical sense of defiance. Maybe I'm reading too much into it but I felt something profoundly disturbing – maybe not in a bad way – a sense that maybe the state couldn't control everybody, that this structure I'd taken for granted all my life maybe wasn't so secure as I'd assumed.

They felt it in Moscow too. As the second half went on, things returned to normal. I don't remember how Edik played or even the score. We took the train home and, although we talked about what had happened, and Edik's capacity to stir passions, I'm not sure anybody at the club or the factory really thought too much of it. But I suppose that sort of thing had the potential to take root. These challenges to authority could not be allowed to pass unremarked. Leonid Ilyichev, the head of the government propaganda department, attacked Volsky, who was investigated by the Bureau of the City Party Committee.

Misha was right. That demonstration in Gorky had its effect. Soon after, a petition was drawn up, signed by tens of thousands of workers as well as heroes of socialist labour, deputies of the Supreme Soviet of the USSR and the RSFSR. 'Who is interested in the fact that Streltsov does not play football, and fans of this sport do not receive aesthetic satisfaction?' it asked. 'He was guilty, he was punished. Does a person have to pay for a mistake for the rest of his life? Why should you deprive a person of their favourite business? ...He should have the right to play football within the limits of his abilities. If some people on whom the decision depends do not agree with this, then we ask you to give them, together with the Chairman of the Supreme Council of Physical Culture and Sport, Comrade Mashin, instructions to come to us, employees of the Likhachev automobile plant, talk to our staff, counting, by the way, many thousands of people, and listen to our opinion.'

The Party responded in the time-honoured way, with a report that was passed on to Volsky and through him to Misha and then to us in the office. 'Streltsov's participation in these games is used by a large part of the fans to glorify Streltsov,' it read. 'Many spectators present at stadiums greet Streltsov's appearance on the football field with applause and shouts of approval.' It made specific reference to the game in Gorky. 'Everything is organised in order to promote Streltsov and achieve his inclusion in the senior team of class "A".'

The recommendations were damning. 'We believe that the inclusion of Streltsov in the Torpedo football team will make it necessary for him to travel abroad, which would create an unhealthy sensation around Streltsov there, since his story at the time found wide coverage in the foreign press. At the same time, the inclusion of morally unscrupulous people in the strongest teams would seriously damage the work of educating young people and athletes, and the prestige of Soviet sports both in our country and abroad.'

The report concluded that it would be wrong for Streltsov to play for the Torpedo first team and made various recommendations about how the Moscow City Committee of the CPSU should explain that to the Party Committee and the management of the Likhachev automobile plant, so that they could ensure 'the proper attitude of factory staff to the issues of education of athletes and the development of physical culture and sports at the plant.' It was signed by Ilyichev and Leonid Brezhnev who, at the time, was chairman of the praesidium of the Supreme Soviet.

So Edik kept playing in the factory championship. Not surprisingly, his quality control department won every game, 11 out of 11, with a goal-difference of 34 to 5. And he went to league matches, not just Torpedo but other games, watching, analysing, working out how, in his physical condition, he could be most effective. That was a part of his game I think people didn't really understand. He was never just about power and pace. He also understood the geometry of the game.

His life was very different. Other former players were allowed to keep their separate apartments, but not Edik. For him perhaps there was the thought that at least it wasn't a barracks at the camp, but Sofia Frolovna ended up having to share with an alcoholic from the factory. But I think the thing that hurt Edik the most was that he wasn't one of the lads any more. The players had their own concerns, their own friendships. The dynamic of their lives was different to that of a quality control technician. Things had changed while Edik had been away, old relationships had broken up, they'd won a championship without him. Who wanted this ghost hanging around? And, looking from the outside, I think he made them nervous. They could go out and drink and have fun and if somebody did something silly, it was no big deal. But if Edik was there... well, who knew how the authorities might react? He and Raisa went to dinner once at Kuzma's place but without football to bind them they had little to talk about. Raisa once told Vera how she felt like Cinderella whenever she met the players' wives in their nice clothes. And there was an occasion when Kuzma's wife Lida ignored her when she queued at her counter at the Central Stores.

Streltsov was in limbo, a football player and not a football player. He had the mentality of a top sportsman and his performances in the factory league showed how talented he remained. He still had that power, that touch, that instinct, but he couldn't play on the stage he deserved. Perhaps some level of decompression was necessary for him. Perhaps it would have been too much to go straight from the camp to the league, and he never said much about it, but he must have been desperately frustrated.

And people at the club started getting frustrated, especially when we started 1963 so badly. Even with Morozov things only improved slightly. The problem that anybody would have had was that they weren't Viktor Maslov. We went through one of those spells in which we played quite well but just couldn't score. The blockage cleared suddenly in the last game before the summer break and Kuzma got a hat-trick as we beat Dynamo Kyiv 7-1 but that was only our fourth win in seventeen games that season. We'd drawn seven, so there was no real danger of relegation, but anybody could see that with a really lethal centre-forward, somebody to take the chances, somebody like Edik, we'd have been turning some of those defeats into draws and some of those draws into wins. Misha would tell me how often the issue was raised at club meetings, only for the discussion to be ended when somebody reminded everybody that Edik was still officially banned and that the factory was supposed to be improving the education of its members.

During the break, Torpedo went south to play some friendlies and raise a little money. I stayed in Moscow that year, so I only know what I was told subsequently. The truth is I don't really know what happened in that famous game in Odessa, and it's one of those occasions that has become almost completely hidden by the myths that grew up around it.

I wish I'd been there, of course. I wish I could tell you that I'd heard all the arguments and the wrangling, the process by which they made the decision. But I was back in Moscow. In truth, when you look back on it, the big decision was taking him to Crimea in the first place, including him in a squad, albeit of the loosest kind. But at the time taking him to train away from the winter didn't seem all that remarkable. Which was where they were so clever, I suppose. I sensed Volsky's hand in that, testing the water and then, when there was no backlash from the Party, they decided to risk it.

Edik was selected for the match against Chernomorets and of course he played brilliantly, scoring twice in a 2-0 win, the first a volley, the second a dipping free-kick. Afterwards the story got about that Boris Batanov had jumped on Edik in celebration and Edik, wary of physical contact since his time in the camps, had shrugged him off. It was one of those stories that captured a truth. He was not the same man he had been before. He was more suspicious. But Batanov wasn't like that. He wasn't the sort to leap on a teammate in celebration. So I don't know exactly what went on, whether there was anything to it or not. The most important thing, though, was that, a year after what had happened in Gorky, Edik had played for Torpedo again, even if it was only in a friendly.

Глава вторая

1964

──────────────── TORPEDO ────────────────

Soviet League: *P32 W19 D8 L5 F52 A19 Pts46.* **Final position:** *2nd of 17.*
Soviet Cup: *Lost in second round to Žalgiris Vilnius.*

Viktor Maryenko, our former defender, who had been team director, came in as manager at the beginning of 1964, and things improved immediately. He'd been a defender through the late fifties, had played a lot with Edik and been there over the time of his trial, and you could see immediately the work he did on the structure of the side. You look back on a season like that and you always wonder what might have been. What if we'd had Edik? What if we'd had somebody who could stick the ball in the net? At the beginning of September we lost away at Dinamo Moscow – having been ahead – and then at Torpedo Kutaisi. Even a point in either of those matches would have been enough. As it turned out, we ended up having played all our games, three points ahead of Dinamo Tbilisi who had two left to play. I remember those days at the office, tensely crowded around the radio, listening as they went behind in Kutaisi but came back to draw. Then they went 2-0 up against Dinamo Moscow, conceded after about an hour and hung on before adding a third in the final minute.

So that meant a play-off, what they called a "golden match". The teams went off to Tashkent in the middle of November, leaving us with the snow, the radio and the samovar – and a few bottles of vodka. Vlada Shcherbakov put us ahead eleven minutes into the second half but Ilya Datunashvili levelled, which was the way it seemed to be that season. We just could never quite shake them off. It went to extra-time and we ended up losing 4-1. To make it worse, the fourth was a penalty converted by Slava Metreveli who'd only left us two years earlier.

There was disappointment, of course, particularly given the feeling that we'd slightly run out of steam towards the end of the season. Could we have been fitter? Those defeats to Dinamo and Torpedo Kutaisi weighed heavy. But at the same time there was a recognition of how much we'd improved from the previous season. Nobody had thought at the beginning of the season that we were going to be challenging for the title. There was a dinner to celebrate winning the silver medals – not that we office staff were invited of course, although they did drop in a bottle of vodka for us to share – and I think the mood was generally joyful. But there was a bit of a fuss that Edik wasn't invited, although not from him. I think Volsky played it right, though. He was young, only thirty-two, but he was smart. Yes, there was a desire to make Edik feel accepted, formally to acknowledge his readmission to the club, but really what would have been served by it? It would have been provocative to the higher authorities, it would have put Edik in an awkward situation with alcohol, particularly given we knew he had started drinking again on occasions, and everybody would have been terrified in case he did something foolish. And for what? To give a suspended player a nice night? No: far better to let those lads enjoy their success. It was their achievement, not Edik's.

Besides which, there was still a collective amnesia about him. Officially Streltsov the footballer didn't exist. Everybody may have been talking about his performances for the quality control team in the factory, and about his appearances in friendlies for the first team, but none of it was mentioned even in the factory newspaper. Only the magazine *Football* dared breach the silence, publishing a letter from a fan asking what had happened to the great Streltsov. A reply was printed, noting that Streltsov was working diligently at the ZIL factory and there were no complaints about his work – as if anybody cared how good he was at quality control!

But I did hear a story from the night of the dinner. They say that Boris Khrenov, the defender who had marked Simonyan out of the game all those years earlier and was by then working as a coach with the club, had proposed a toast to Edik and his return to football. Not long after, Misha told me that Maryenko had started lobbying the leaders at ZIL hard to ask again for Edik's ban to be lifted, vowing that with him he could win the championship. Viktor Semyonovich had played with Edik for four years before the incident and had written to him in the camp, even after he'd left Torpedo for Avangard Kharkiv. I'm not sure you'd say he and Edik were friends, exactly, but there was definitely a healthy mutual respect.

You had to be careful with such things, though, and that's where Volsky was so important. He was good at the politics, understood the timing. Leonid Brezhnev was elected by the October Plenum of the Central Committee to replace Khrushchev and there was a reception to mark the occasion. Volsky was invited and used the occasion to mention his banned footballer, suggesting how popular lifting the suspension would be. And that was when Brezhnev uttered his famous line: 'When a technician has served his sentence, can he no longer work as a technician?'

Volsky had won, but consummate operator that he was, he pressed home his advantage. He knew that it had been Brezhnev's signature on the report of July the previous year that had recommended the ban remain in place, so he asked about the issue of Leonid Ilyichev, who was implacably opposed to Edik's return. And Brezhnev replied that he would find a way to control him. Now perhaps it was coincidence but the following spring, as Edik returned to action, Ilyichev found himself demoted from being head of propaganda to being a deputy foreign minister.

Глава третья

1965

Soviet League: *P32 W22 D7 L3 F55 A21 Pts40.* **Final position:** *1st of 17.*
Soviet Cup: *Lost in second round to Shakhter Karagandy.*

Of course, it wasn't straightforward. How could it have been? Just because Brezhnev said something didn't make it instantly true, particularly given Brezhnev understandably never said anything about the case in public, leaving everything to the state apparatus. That meant bureaucracy to be worked through, and I know that drove Misha to despair at times. And even when Edik was allowed to play, there was of course still a ban on him leaving the country.

That meant that when Torpedo went on their pre-season tour to Australia, Edik had to stay behind. He went to Khosta with the youth team, who were coached by Lekha Anisimov, who had played for Torpedo when Edik had first joined from the Fraser factory. When the first team returned from Australia, I went down to join them at the Sputnik Hotel at Khosta for a ten-day camp. Edik moved in with them. He didn't say much, as ever, but he was so desperate to play that he joined Boris Batanov, who was recovering from a groin strain, in cross-country runs along the railway line towards Kudepsta. Before, Edik had always tried to get out of cross-country runs because of his flat feet but here he was, willingly doing extra training.

The first game of that season was away in Baku against Neftyanik. I'd gone to the stadium early to make sure the dressing-room was clean, the hot water was on, the kit was laid out, all the protocols had been signed, the usual stuff and I remember him getting off the bus, wearing an unbuttoned jacket and a light scarf, his sports bag over his shoulder, a look on his face of – well, what, exactly? Relief? Joy? Happiness? A sense of lightness certainly. I prepared myself for the perfect return, for Edik scoring a brilliant goal as he had in Odessa. But there was nothing. Vladimir Brukhti marked him out of the game as we lost 3-0 – Banishevsky scored the first, and they got two further goals late on as we chased the game. It wasn't really a 3-0 match but it was all very anti-climactic. It would take Edik time to re-adjust, we told ourselves, but we were all thinking that maybe he would never get it back.

Then we went back to Moscow for the first home game, against Krylya Sovetov. Edik got ill, just a cold, but I did wonder if it had been brought on by stress. As the others milled around the cottage at Myachkovo, talking to journalists, he remained in his room, trying to sleep it off. He played the next day, at Luzhniki. Volodya Shcherbakov, who had been moved out to the wing in Baku, was dropped – although I don't think he minded too much. I heard a story that he helped himself to one of the publicity photos Edik had signed.

Everybody, of course was desperate for him to succeed. The cheers when he came onto the pitch and when he touched the ball for the first time were extraordinary. I wondered what Eva would think, the way the desire to welcome his return outweighed any thoughts of what he might have done.

He didn't play well. He looked heavy, sluggish. And top-level football was changing then. We were lucky: Viktor Maslov had shown us the 4-2-4 and its possibilities before most other Soviet sides but, still, the game in 1965 was very different to the game in 1958. I sat with Misha and within ten minutes I was pointing out to him what I'd feared in Baku, that Edik didn't understand the system. The game was going on around him. His movement was wrong. He was demanding the ball in the wrong positions. You could almost see the breakdown in his off-pitch relationship with Kuzma being played out on it.

But a great footballer remains a great footballer. Quarter of an hour in, he killed an awkward ball from Kuzma, advanced on the Krylya goal, paused, and played to his left one of those passes with his heel for which he was so famous. Kuzma ran on and finished into the corner. They'd been scoring goals like that for a decade, but this one meant far more than any that had gone before. Kuzma ran straight to him and seized his cheeks in his hands. They would never be friends as they had been in the fifties, but in football they were born to play together.

Two minutes later, Vlada Mikhailov headed in after a corner from Oleg Sergeev, who had come in for Shcherbakov, had hit the bar and that was the game won. But we didn't really play well. And that pattern continued. We drew 0-0 away to Pakhtakor and then, with Edik and Kuzma and a couple of others injured, we drew 0-0 against CSKA back in Moscow. At the time, I was worried it would be the same as the previous season: playing decently but lacking the finisher to turn draws into wins.

That doubt didn't last long. I think we felt we owed Torpedo Kutaisi something after the way they'd derailed our title bid the previous season, and that showed. Kuzma was back but Edik was still missing, which meant Shcherbakov playing through the middle again. He scored twice, as did Kuzma, and we won 5-0.

But 5-0 without Edik. What did that mean? Could it be they were better without him? Kuzma missed the next game, away in Odessa, and Edik returned. He and Shcherbakov linked well and we won 2-0, although largely thanks to defensive errors. And that was when Maryenko found a way to fit in Kuzma and Edik, and Batanov, Shcherbakov and Sergeev – as well as Voronin in midfield. Voronin then was at his peak, an elegant, graceful intelligent player with the physical capacity to dominate. We went to Donetsk to play Shakhtar and beat them 3-0. We had five top-level forwards and it was our sixth straight clean sheet. That was the game when I first thought something remarkable might be happening.

The bosses soon arranged for Edik to move into a two-room apartment on Mashinostroitelnaya ulitsa, and this time his mother didn't join him. Sofia Frolovna remained in her small apartment, and I think that was good for Edik's state of mind. In the middle of June, we beat Dynamo Kyiv 1-0 with a fine goal from Shcherbakov and that night the players and their wives met at Edik's place. They celebrated but there was also a serious conversation. It had become pretty clear that we and Dynamo Kyiv would be the two main contenders for the title, and we were all aware that the way Maslov coached sides, Dynamo would probably get stronger as the season went on. So there was a discussion and it was decided that Voronin and Vladimir Brednev would play a little deeper, to try to control games a little more. There was great spirit, and there was a clear plan.

What we still needed, though, was a goal from Edik. We kept winning. We didn't let in goals. We kept eight clean sheets in a row. We drew against Dinamo Tbilisi, but mostly we kept winning. It was cool, modern football. It might have lacked the flourish of old, but it was efficient and there was a romance perhaps in that. Nobody quite knew what to make of Edik. He was playing in a winning team. Every now and again he would play a clever pass. But he didn't quite look part of the same mechanism as everybody else. You couldn't help but compare him to what he had been and he was no longer that. The explosiveness had gone, his pace had gone, and it seemed almost like he was deliberately trying to keep a low profile, passing when he might have gone on alone, laying the ball off when he might have shot. It was as though he were determined nobody should ever accuse him of selfishness again.

....

That July, Brazil came to Luzhniki for a friendly. So many people wanted to see them even I couldn't get a ticket, so had to watch on TV at the club. They had a number of stars: Bellini, Gérson, Jairzinho and, of course, Pelé. There were those who said they should have let Edik play against him, the two great forwards on one pitch, but at the time that was never a serious consideration, not just because of the politics but because Edik hadn't scored a top-flight goal for more than seven years. There were still plenty of people at Torpedo who wondered if we mightn't be better off without him.

But Edik went to the game and took his place in the stand. He watched Kuzma struggle in the heat and be withdrawn at half-time for Banishevsky – who of course did nothing. By then Pelé had already scored twice and Flavio added another in the second half. We were well-beaten 3-0, but at least we got to see Pelé score.

And six days after the Brazilian Streltsov had scored twice in Moscow, the Russian Pelé did as well. It was late afternoon at the Dinamo Stadium, a warm day of frequent showers. I remember constantly fiddling about with an umbrella. We went behind very early to a header from Eduard Malofeev and Minsk kept on troubling us with their pace out wide. We never really found our rhythm all game. Voronin, for some reason, played too far forward and everything seemed a little anxious. The composure, the ability to set the tempo that had characterised us all season had gone.

But then just after the hour, Vladimir Brednev hung up a cross, Voronin nodded it down and Edik ran on and smashed it first time into the corner. It helped, I think, that he had no time to think. It was just instinct: a dropping ball and bang! And of course the celebrations in the stands when everybody realised who had scored were extra special. And then two minutes from time, he got the winner, poking in the rebound after efforts from Shcherbakov and Sergeev had been blocked. We'd won, we were still top, and Edik had scored twice.

What else can I say about that season? When Edik scored, it was like the storm had broken after a humid day. Everybody felt the relief. Two games later, after Batanov had stolen a late equaliser against Zenit, Edik scored a goal against Lokomotiv that could have come from his 1957 catalogue: a burst of pace, a sudden finish. He missed a penalty against Chornomorets but then knocked in the rebound, then missed another penalty against SKA from Rostov.

Then there was the game away against Shakhtar, one that was a reminder of all the politicking that was always going on. Vladimir Meshcheryakov, who was a very good defender, had started gossiping about little additional payments Kuzma and Voronin would get from the factory bosses, making a point of telling Edik how he should have been getting these payments as well – and raising the issue when Kuzma and Voronin were away with the national side. I think Meshcheryakov was worried about his place in the team and thought having Edik as an ally would help, but Edik had no interest in getting involved in factional infighting. Maryenko was decisive. He went to the national camp to speak to Kuzma and Voronin and they agreed: squad unity had to be maintained and so Meshcheryakov had to be got rid of. He was transferred to Shakhtar.

And so of course against Torpedo, determined to deny them the title that he could no longer win, Meshcheryakov had the game of his life, completely neutralising Kuzma. It was probably that game that got him a move to Spartak for the following season. But we still won, thanks to Edik scoring one of those goals that reminded you of the sort of player he had once been. He controlled an awkward ball in midfield and advanced as defenders backed off. He twice dummied to shoot, eventually putting

Vladimir Salkov (who told the story himself when he became our coach in the seventies) on his backside, then went back past him and rolled his shot past the keeper.

In the middle of September we went to Kyiv to face Maslov's Dynamo, who led us by a point having played one game more. Win there and we would have a clear advantage, but everybody was worried what Maslov would have planned for Edik and Kuzma, two players he knew better than anybody else. It was his second season there, and they were starting to play some remarkable football. Lobanovskyi had been offloaded to Chernomorets, people said because he and Maslov had had a row – supposedly, although it seems scarcely credible now, because Valeriy Valentinovich had refused a glass of *horilka* after a flight had been delayed and Viktor Aleksandrovich was trying to relax everybody. Maybe there had been an argument – although Maslov really wasn't somebody to pick a fight – but it was also clear that the Lobanovskyi style of winger didn't fit in Maslov's system as he packed midfield with runners and played something akin to what we would probably today call a 4-4-2.

And they did get the better of us. I wish I'd been there to see what happened – it was difficult to tell from the radio – but from talking to people afterwards and reading the report in *Football*, which was by far the best of the sports papers at that time for actually explaining games, I think they pressed us into oblivion, hitting us with wave after wave and denying our midfield, which had been our strength, any space or time. We held out till just after the half hour but when we broke, we broke completely and, shattered, let in three in a six-minute blast. But it seemed the effort of pressing with such intensity took it out of Dynamo as well and, in the second half, we got back into it.

The myth has it that Edik played like a man possessed, determined to prove to his mentor that he was still a great, and perhaps there was something of that in his second-half performance, although I suspect the reality is that Dynamo were exhausted. People didn't really grasp then just how tiring pressing was and, anyway, that's a less attractive story than the heroism of one man. I remember one night on one of those early-season trips to the south Viktor Aleksandrovich excitedly explaining his idea to a group of us in a hotel bar and everybody nodding along, not really understanding what he was talking about as he shuffled our glasses around the table. It wouldn't really be until the following year when Dynamo won the title that people really began to talk about his innovation. Anyway, Edik scored a pair of headers from corners, then Voronin had a goal ruled out and the sense was that if the game had gone on five or ten minutes more Dynamo would have collapsed completely.

But they held out and that gave Dynamo a three-point advantage. We cut it to one the following week with a win at Zenit – it was their week off; the championship that year had 17 teams – and then it was neck and neck. We drew against Neftyanik and Dinamo Tbilisi, when Edik got the equaliser; they drew against Dinamo Moscow and lost, a vital defeat, at Torpedo Kutaisi five games from the end. We came from behind to win in Minsk that day with three goals in the final half hour and that gave us the advantage.

Edik's link-up with Kuzma destroyed Pakhtakor in the final home game and then he got two away to Torpedo Kutaisi. That meant we had one game left and a five-point lead over Dynamo, who had three games to play. The first of them was in Rostov against SKA, three days before our final game. It felt horribly like the previous season as we all gathered in the office to listen to their match on the radio. SKA took the lead then fell behind but with five minutes remaining they equalised. That meant we would need only a point in our final game against Chernomorets in Odessa three days later. But three minutes later Andriy Biba got a winner.

That deflated everybody. We all remembered Dinamo Tbilisi's late winners the previous year.

So we gathered again in the office, a cool Monday evening. A win and we couldn't be caught, but there was also the hope of Dynamo dropping points in their game against Zenit. They then had SKA of Odessa to play the following Saturday. Misha had bought a white rose for luck and Eva, who joined us in the office, wore it in her hair. She'd baked a cake, but we were more interested in the vodka. Everybody was atrociously anxious. Two minutes in, Mikhailov turned sharply and slipped a pass through for Edik. A burst of acceleration beyond a gaggle of defenders and a lightning left-foot strike into the top-right corner. A typical Edik goal, just when we needed it – although paradoxically that seemed to make us more nervous, both the players on the pitch, and us in the office. Eva used to pretend she didn't care, but as pass after pass went astray she began to pace up and down.

When they equalised after twenty minutes, it almost came as a relief, as though we could settle down again and reset. Vyacheslav Marusho hit the post and Kuzma couldn't quite get on the end of it and then, six minutes before half-time, a minute after Dynamo had taken the lead in their game against Zenit, a remarkable goal. Aleksandr Lenev, who'd only joined us that year from Shinnik, where I think he'd only ever scored once, picked the ball up almost on halfway, saw the keeper off his line and chipped him. And as if to prove it wasn't a fluke, he did it again in the second half, but hit the bar.

By then, it felt, at least to those of us 1300km away, as though all reason had gone out of the game and all we could do was trust to the fates. We were just counting down the minutes, drinking, walking about, sighing, nobody saying much, apart from Denis the accountant who would never shut up when he was nervous. Dynamo got a second against Zenit with five minutes to go, so we knew there'd be no help from there. We probably should have extended our lead. We weren't really under pressure, although Chernomorets had a couple of breaks and you were always wary of Lobanovskyi at corners. But we held on. I remember everybody hugging each other, and Eva kissed me on the cheek, then somebody found some champagne from somewhere and we kept drinking into the night. Our second title, and we'd won it in Edik's first year back. He was still only twenty-eight.

Maryenko had said that if he got Edik, he would win the championship and he was right. The oddity was that I'm not sure Edik was even the main reason – even if he did finish up with twelve goals. He gave us something extra up front, of course, and some of his goals, particularly the one against Lokomotiv, were a reminder of the player of old, of the way he could conjure a goal from nowhere. His link-up play was intelligent and in those final weeks, he offered that combination of individual menace and clever team play that I think Maryenko had always envisaged. But actually we won the league because of the solidity of the defence. It was Voronin who, for the second year running, was Footballer of the Year (Edik came second, although they didn't reveal that until much later). That was the way football was going in those days. Maslov, eventually, went further than Maryenko, and his development of pressing was obviously hugely important but Maslov was a genius. Maryenko was smart and, in his own, less radical way, also a pioneer.

And Edik? Well, it wasn't easy for him. There were times when you saw him at the Central Store waiting for Raisa, surrounded by fans as he had been before. But where before, at least some of the time, he had seemed to relish the attention, now he just looked tired. I think he was aware of his appearance was well, conscious of how his looks had waned. When Raisa cut off her braid, he joked he should have it made into a wig, but

I'm not sure how much of a joke it really was – it was as though he was saying it before anybody else had the chance to.

He was not the same player he had been. How could he have been? It wasn't just him, and everything that had diminished his self-confidence and his physical powers. It was that football had changed. Football went in the space of three or four years from being a game about individuals to being about the collective – and actually about the collective, not the team spirit nonsense you always hear but about the interactions of the separate components within the system. Of course, Dynamo Kyiv was the epicentre of that, with Maslov. But where was Maslov from? What was Maryenko doing? Who was the national coach going into the 66 World Cup? It was Nikolai Morozov. Torpedo was the home of these ideas – and perhaps you would say we had learned them from Boris Arkadiev and Mikhail Yakushin, the great Dinamo Moscow and CDKA of the forties and early fifties, for nothing is born of nothing, but our role cannot be denied. Edik left one world and seven years later he returned in another, and we had helped change it.

Edik had to learn his body and what it was capable of, and he had to explore this new world in which the player he had been had no part. You couldn't be an individual any more. You could no longer linger on the periphery as Edik had once done, waiting for his moment. You had to be involved. And he was able to do it. It took a few months but by the end of the season, he was integrated. Was he a better player? I think that would be a stretch, but he was a different player, a subtler player, a less eye-catching player. And that provoked a lot of debate. There were those who claimed to see the underlying patterns who painted him as some all-controlling puppetmaster, and there were others who thought him a fraud living off his reputation and the abilities of his teammates. He scored twelve goals, he knitted together attacks with clever movement and passing and we won the championship. And I knew that from midsummer onwards, from the time that Pelé came to Moscow, I never heard a teammate complain about him. And that was enough for me. Was he the all-time world great we'd hoped he might be? No, but he was an excellent player integral to an excellent side.

He was even named as the left-sided forward in the official team of the year, which seemed a major statement. The factory paper, laughably, barely mentioned Edik's contribution in its write-up of the season. Other newspapers chose to focus on Kuzma or Voronin – and there was some justification for that. They were the senior heads, the brains of the team. Even Edik's most passionate supporters couldn't claim that he had won the title single-handed. At the ceremony to present the medals, though, in front of 15,000 fans at the Luzhniki, it was Edik who received the loudest and longest cheers – a small moment of defiance against the authorities and a gesture of support for somebody returning from the darkness.

It would be nice to finish it all there, to pretend that with the championship, all sins were absolved, that our hero, having gone through his trial, had earned his redemption. And for many people that was true. There is no better way for a man to cleanse his reputation than for him to be successful.

At times, I allowed myself to be carried along by it. And this was a great story: a man who had undergone terrible privations returning and leading his team to an unlikely championship. But Eva never forgot, I'm sure Marina Lebedeva never forgot, and I never entirely forgot. Even if you believe that it was all a conspiracy, that Edik was set up, there is one point in which his conduct was never forgivable, and that was in the matter of Alla and Mila.

I'm sure Alla didn't make it easy for him, but why should she have made it easy for him? He should have begged and begged and begged her for forgiveness and, even if she wanted nothing to do with him, at least have paid his due for Mila. But Mila had been born two months before his disgrace, and so she came to symbolise it. In 1965 she was seven, and those were the seven years in which he had not been allowed to play football.

There was one day Vera came into the office and told us she'd met Alla and Mila at a tram stop the previous day (Alla had moved to Kuzminki a couple of years earlier and I think Vera had a brother out that way). Alla had explained that they'd gone to the Mashenka shop on Smolenskaya to buy a school uniform for Mila who was about to start first grade. They'd bumped into Edik, who had been drunk but had insisted on coming with them, even though Mila was afraid of him in that state. He'd smelled of booze, had talked too loudly, had criticised the uniform and had been generally embarrassing, fumbling in his pocket until Alla ended up paying. Edik had accompanied them home, so he found out where they lived.

After that we heard he would wait for Alla outside the factory, which she hated. I'm sure he meant well, but she told Vera she felt he was monitoring her. For a man who had so much experience of women, he never quite lost his social awkwardness around them. With Alla, he could be cold and he could be smothering and, I'm sure because of his sense of guilt, he never quite seemed able to work out how he was supposed to treat her.

Глава четвертая

1966

TORPEDO

Soviet League: *P36 W15 D10 L11 F55 A39 Pts40.* **Final position:** *6th of 19.*
Soviet Cup: *Lost in final to Dynamo Kyiv.*

Every victory has its shadow. After the great high of 1965, we knew that what followed must be disappointment. And 1966 was, in every way, a very disappointing year for Torpedo. The only consolation was that Viktor Maslov enjoyed such success at Dynamo Kyiv.

It started to go wrong for us with a home defeat to Shakhtar at the beginning of May and we never really put together a consistent run after that. In part that was because we lost Voronin – and our goalkeeper Anzor Kavazashvili – to the World Cup squad, but other teams lost their best players as well. We ended up finishing sixth as Maslov's Dynamo ran away with it – they only lost three league games all season.

A week before the World Cup, we played away at Lokomotiv and Edik was sent off. Stupid, really. Maybe it's too easy to say the World Cup was playing on his mind. Maybe life isn't that simple. But Edik wasn't right that day. He got kicked and Maryenko made a big point about saying that when he saw him in the shower afterwards, even his balls were black and blue, but Edik always got kicked. That was an annoying game. We were too predictable against a team that was happy to defend and then Vladimir Brednev missed a penalty midway through the second half. We couldn't break them down. But still, Edik shouldn't have lashed out as he did. You couldn't argue with the decision. Valentin Denisov scored a winner with three minutes remaining but taking the two points seemed less important at that moment than the potential backlash.

We were all anxious about what sanction they might impose. Misha admitted he feared they may ban him again completely and say his re-education hadn't gone far enough. But the newspapers were restrained. *Football* claimed Edik had been 'taking too many liberties recently' and had a silly paragraph moralising about how great players didn't lose their temper like that. But that was it. He got the statutory ban and everybody moved on. I think that's when we knew that Edik really was back.

The World Cup was a frustration as well. The draw was kind to us and then we won a tight quarter-final against Hungary before losing to West Germany in the semi-final and Portugal in the match for third. People began wondering then about what might have happened if Edik had played, and Morozov later said he'd have welcomed him back, but I don't think he ever did much lobbying on Edik's behalf, so we ended up with Banishevsky up front and, well, I've made my opinion about his abilities clear enough.

You can't blame Morozov, I suppose. National coach is a hard enough position anyway, with every fan thinking you should have picked more players from their club and suits who knew nothing about football suddenly taking an interest. Just look at how Yashin was treated after the World Cup in 62 after letting in that goal against Colombia. So I see that Morozov didn't want to insist on Streltsov, and risk him failing to perform or doing something daft in England. But it was as though the World Cup opened a door. People who mattered suddenly decided we needed him and that, now people had worked out he wasn't a defection risk, overrode everything else.

Edik was changing. Where once he said he had liked big wins because it gave every forward a chance to score so nobody would be left out, he admitted he had started feeling sorry for humiliated opponents. As his strength waned, he said he preferred goals that didn't crash into the back of the net but that were scored with deft precision, so the ball barely trickled over the line but the keeper was nonetheless helpless. That August he scored the second in a 2-0 win over Dynamo Kyiv and did just that, dumping Viktor Bannikov one way and rolling the ball in the other corner.

He scored less often, but didn't seem to mind. He had found other satisfactions. He registered his first ever league hat-trick against SKA of Odessa and got twelve for the season. With the advent of zonal marking he was no longer just playing up against one defender he could physically dominate. And maybe he wouldn't have had the power any more to do that anyway. In the lists they came up with of the three teams of the season, Edik was selected as the right-sided striker in the first XI, ahead of Anatoly Byshovets of Dynamo Kyiv, who was only 20 but was already an exceptional player.

But Edik wasn't changing that much. His period of abstinence was long since over and we started to worry about him again. But what can you do? He wanted to be one of the lads again. He liked to drink. Years in a camp didn't change that. That summer there was a night when he went missing. It turned out he'd been drinking at Konstantin Beskov's apartment and had fallen asleep in the hallway. Volsky even called Beskov to ask him to stop drinking with Edik, but you couldn't separate football people from their alcohol.

That autumn there came a major breakthrough. By winning the league, Torpedo had qualified for the European Cup for the first time. The draw was tough: we got Inter, the defending champions. And of course the question was asked: would Edik be allowed to travel to Milan? There was a meeting of the Party Committee in Moscow, which I heard about from Misha. Raisa Dementieva, the Second Secretary, was very much against him going, but she was shouted down. I don't know. The older I get the less these things seem explicable. Maybe they really did think he had served his time. Maybe there was a sense that no good was served by the Soviet champions going abroad and losing heavily. Or maybe, as Eva suggested, it was just that the men who liked football outweighed the women who cared about rape.

Anyway, they put Volsky in charge of the delegation and said it was his decision and his responsibility. He was initially reluctant, knowing that if Edik defected in Italy, his career would be over, but Borodin, one of the ZIL directors, taunted him, asking if he, a man noted for his determination and courage, was scared a footballer might run away.

Volsky took the bait and agreed Edik could play in Milan. He was partnered up front not by Kuzma but by Vladimir Shcherbakov who was only 21 but had been called up to the national side the previous September. The other thing that was going on that season was Kuzma's decline. He was only 31 but somehow when he came back that year he wasn't the player he had been. He was left out of the national squad, struggled to get into our team and retired at the end of the year. It was all very sudden and very sad.

We'd got Valentin Denisov back from CSKA that season. He was a decent player but a little overweight, good at linking with others and he played well that night against a great side. Brednev had that shot that hit the bar and looked as though it had bounced over the line but wasn't given – which, given what we later found out about Inter and referees, made you wonder – but they won it with a Sandro Mazzola goal in the second half that deflected in off Voronin.

We drew 0-0 in Moscow and were out, undone by the draw and a refereeing decision, but the most significant thing was that Edik was back. Of course, being Edik, he couldn't avoid controversy entirely. The morning after the game Colonel Boris Orlov, who was in charge of security, came knocking on Volsky's door in a fury: Edik was missing. They searched the hotel. He wasn't there. Eventually Volsky, who must have been fearing dreadful repercussions, decided there was no option but to return to Moscow without him. But Edik was there at the airport, oblivious to the panic. He'd gone drinking with some Inter players. Of course he had. A journalist had seen him and asked whether he would consider defecting. 'Why would I do that?' he asked. 'In the West presidents get shot.' For Edik and the state it was the perfect answer: the Italian papers all carried the story about his reference to Kennedy, and back home all sins were forgiven. But it was another example of his basic lack of responsibility. How can he not have realised that on his first trip abroad after jail, he should have been on his very best behaviour? There were times when his naivety was inexplicable.

Still, once they'd allowed Edik to start travelling abroad again, there was no reason to prevent him playing for the national side. That September, he was called up for the friendly against Turkey in Moscow a couple of weeks after the game in Milan. It was a really poor performance, a 2-0 defeat, one of those games you sometimes get with the national team when nothing quite gels – and Edik was too diffident, too concerned with not looking arrogant or entitled, to seize the game himself. Or at least that's what we said. By then, maybe, he wasn't able any more to turn a game single-handed any more.

But Edik stayed in the team for the game a week later when the great Viktor Ponedelnik said goodbye with a five-minute cameo at the start. Do people still remember him? He headed the winner in the final of the 1960 European Championship – a really clever player from Rostov, but he'd had appendicitis the previous year and struggled to regain fitness. He went off to great applause to be replaced by Anatoly Byshovets, who was a wonderful footballer, but very different to Streltsov – although I always felt the contrast the press described between the two was overblown. Edik scored the opening goal but we drew 2-2 without ever really looking convincing. He and Byshovets played together again in a 1-0 defeat in Italy a week after that. Three games back, one draw and two defeats: it was all in keeping with a year in which nothing quite seemed to work out.

We did get to the Cup semi-final, so it was another afternoon in the office, gathered around the television to watch the game from Leningrad. There must have been a dozen of us there with tea and vodka. Everybody was smoking and it was a chilly October day so the windows were shut. It was like a fog had come down. It was one of those slightly odd games. We were much better than Chornomorets, and we went ahead in the first half through Brednev. Everybody was joking, only half-watching. We just assumed we'd win. And then with about ten minutes to go there was a collective realisation that it was still only 1-0 and Chornomorets might pinch an equaliser. In those circumstances, having dominated almost counts against you because you start thinking of all the opportunities to finish the game that you wasted. Then Edik turned in his own half. I swear all of us relaxed at that moment. We all knew, almost started celebrating before it was in. Something in his demeanour, even through the fuzz of the television, even though he didn't really make those bursts any more, we knew. Off he went, charging through, defenders collapsing around him and sure enough, 2-0. It was beautiful, a reminder of why we had all loved him. He got another one in the last minute as well.

But Maslov did us again in the final. Byshovets scored in the first minute and Andriy Biba added a second to wrap it up.

There had been a moment, though, when Edik and Shcherbakov broke against the central defender Vadym Sosnikhin, the sort of overmanning situation that once, with Edik and Kuzma, would have been an almost certain goal. Edik feigned to pass but Sosnikhin read the disguise and dispossessed him. Edik was haunted by that: they say he stayed up all night drinking wine, stewing on it, listening to that Ukrainian song 'Cheremshina' that was everywhere at the time. And I think we were to some extent all haunted by it, by the failure to find an equaliser, by this reminder of how age diminishes us all.

Глава пятая

1967

TORPEDO

Soviet League: *P36 W12 D9 L15 F38 A47 Pts33.* **Final position:** *12th of 19.*
Soviet Cup: *Lost in quarter-final to Dinamo Moscow.*

As I got older, I increasingly found myself out of step with the general mood. More and more I developed my own ideas of how things were that didn't necessarily fit with what the government or the newspapers or my colleagues told me. Often I didn't bother to express what I thought. On important matters it could be dangerous and if the subject were trivial, why provoke unpleasantness? And so this comes as an admission. By 1967, I had lost my faith in Edik as a footballer.

Maybe it's not coincidence that it happened just as Mikhail Yakushin took charge of the national side, as Morozov returned to Torpedo to replace Maryenko. I was always a Torpedo fan, but after the War, I'd watched Mikhail Iosifovich's Dinamo sides with a sense of awe. He had shaped what I believed football should be. By 1967, it's true, his time was probably past. He was still only in his late fifties but Maslov and pressing were obviously the future. That was the advantage the USSR had over the rest of the world and we didn't use it. But Yakushin had never quite seen eye-to-eye with Edik. I'm not sure anybody ever really knew why but he didn't rate him as others did. It was obvious he preferred Igor Chislenko. Round Torpedo they said it was because Chislenko was a Dinamo player. Maybe it was, but he was also a very good, very intelligent centre-forward. I'm not sure, when you strip away the myth, that by then he wasn't better than Edik.

Under Yakushin, the USSR improved dramatically. We won in Glasgow and Paris, then beat Austria 4-3 at Luzhniki in the European Championship, when Malofeev, Byshovets and Chislenko all scored, only for Austria to pull it back to 3-3 after an error from Yashin, before Edik headed a winner. But, really, how could you play all four forwards together? Maybe it seems ridiculous to complain when we got those results in the first six months under Yakushin, when, if I remember rightly, *France Football* ranked us as the best side in Europe that year, but you could see problems being stored up, the top-heaviness of the side, the way Edik spent all his time trying to fit in with others. By the autumn, when we lost in Vienna, you could see that there was no real fluency to the attack. We got a draw against England at Wembley – what might have been the previous summer! – thanks to two goals from Chislenko, and then Edik scored a brilliant hat-trick away to Chile but I looked at that side and saw individuals bailing us out, nothing like the team dynamic Yakushin was famous for.

But the real problem that year was Torpedo. We finished twelfth in the league. It was a shambles. Valery Voronin had fallen out with Morozov and ran a fairly unsubtle campaign to have him replaced. There was the usual stuff about training not being sufficiently intense, about there being no overall plan. In that football has never changed: when it goes wrong the players will always blame the coach, and they will always use the same phrases to do so. It was all very unpleasant, and Morozov was forced out at the end of July. In his place was appointed Kuzma, who was only 33 and had no experience at all. There were those who saw Edik's hand in that, but he was never a conspirator. If he was guilty of anything it was only of not putting an end to the plotting. And maybe there was something attractive in reuniting the triumvirate – Edik, Kuzma, Voronin – who had brought the title in 1965.

We lost to Dinamo Moscow in the quarter-final of the Cup, a game for which Voronin didn't show up and Edik played with a Novocain injection. We lost to Cardiff City – of Wales! – in the quarter-final of the Cup Winners' Cup (which we were only in because Dynamo Kyiv had done the double the previous season). It was all such a waste.

Voronin seemed to just fall into a pit, as though suddenly he just didn't want to play football any more. He struggled to sleep, he took a lot of pills, he started drinking heavily. He went off to Sochi with his girlfriend in the middle of the season and was given a dressing down by Volsky. Really the World Cup in England was the last we saw of him at his best. He went missing before the second leg of the quarter-final against Hungary (although he wasn't the only one), and was later found to have been drinking in the attic at the training camp. When Yakushin, after the game, told him to go back to Myachkovo, Voronin took a few days off, which in his case meant drinking. Driving at dawn, he fell asleep at the wheel and they say his life was saved only because his seat wasn't fixed after a liaison with, well, let's say a well-known woman, the night before. The mangled wreck of his black Volga, for some reason, was dumped at Myachkovo and left there for weeks, so anybody who went to the training ground would see it. Voronin never really got over the crash. He retired three years later and after that you'd see him around, trying his hand at journalism, coaching the works teams, a husk of the man he had been.

And then, of course, came the end, that May morning in 1984 when he was found by the side of the Varshavskoe highway with his head stoved in by a beer glass. Those were bleak days: just a few days earlier Sergei Salnikov had collapsed and died as he took off his boots after a Spartak veterans game. Poor Edik, losing his old mates one by one.

Edik only scored six times in 1967. His turn and volley against CSKA was brilliant. His goal against Motor Zwickau in the first round of the Cup

Winners' Cup, flicking the ball over two defenders and lashing it in as it dropped, was even better. He was magnificent in both games against Spartak Trnava in the second round. The home leg was in November so we played it in Tashkent and won 3-1; Edik didn't score but his influence was such that they gave him a tambourine for being the best forward in the game. Who knows what the Uzbeks thought he would do with a tambourine, but it was a nice gesture. Then in Czechoslovakia he got two in a 3-0 win. But he had changed as a player.

Maybe I was getting old. Maybe I just didn't understand the evolution of the game. But I watched and respected Maslov's Dynamo and a decade later I appreciated Lobanovskyi and the Netherlands. I understood pressing, to the extent that any layman did. Did it excite me the way Bobrov or Beskov or Edik once had, or the way Shengelia and Daraselia later would? No, perhaps not, but your forties are not a time when you are much excited. Then again, I loved watching Byshovets.

People said then that Edik had become less of an athlete and more of a footballer. But it seemed to me he slowed everything down. With the loss of the directness that had made him great, Edik seemed to revel in indirectness, as though football were won not by how many goals you scored but by how many passes you could string together. You don't understand, they told me. Even Misha disagreed with me. And then somehow Edik was named footballer of the year.

They laughed as though that proved their point. But there was inconsistency here. All Edik's fans happily believed his career had been held back by politics, and they were right. But as soon as the politics went in his favour they were blind to it. Martin Merzhanov had stood down as editor of *Football* and been replaced by Lev Filatov. Now, I believe Filatov was the best football journalist of that generation. He understood the game better than the others, and he had more integrity. He believed in the game itself, not in the ideological battles it could be used to fight. But I wonder if here he over-compensated, that he felt the sport owed Edik for the years of neglect. And I wonder if that dovetailed with a more general unease about how Dynamo Kyiv were playing, a sense that pressing somehow wasn't really football. You'll ask me who I would have given it to that year and the truth is I don't know. The years blur together, and I don't recall these things as clearly as I'd like, but probably somebody from Dynamo – Biba again, or Byshovets or Muntyan. Or maybe Murtaz Khurtsilava from Dinamo Tbilisi. But not Edik.

But he had been rehabilitated. They made him an Honoured Master of Sport again.

Глава шестая

1968

—————————————— **TORPEDO** ——————————————

Soviet League: *P38 W18 D14 L6 F60 A32 Pts50.* **Final position:** *3rd of 20.*
Soviet Cup: *Won, beating Pakhtakor in the final.*

Edik was Footballer of the Year again in 1968 – and that perhaps was more merited as he scored twenty-one goals in the league and we finished third, although we were still seven points behind Maslov's Dynamo. Mikhail Gershkovich was signed from Lokomotiv and, while he took a little time to integrate, he and Edik developed a rapport. Between them they demolished Spartak with two goals each in a 5-1 to avenge the 6-2 defeat the previous season. But Spartak still finished two points above us.

Edik's form for the national team, though, was indifferent in another indifferent year. Maybe Maslov's radicalism was too much for them, maybe there was some reason why they wouldn't have been able to get him away from Kyiv to make him national coach, but you looked at that side and those players and couldn't help wonder what might have happened in a properly modern system. But that was a melancholic thought: Mikhey Yakushin wasn't modern any more. The march of history overtakes us all.

The problems were there in a friendly against Belgium when Banishevsky – seriously, what did these people see in him? – started instead of Malofeev and we won 1-0 only thanks to a last-minute penalty from Josef Szabo. That preparation for the quarter-final of the European Championship against Hungary. In Budapest, when there was no Byshovets, we were dismal and lost 2-0. Both Hungarian goals were the fault of Anzor Kavazashvili, Torpedo's keeper, and Edik had one of those terrible games he'd sometimes had when he was a kid, when he seemed almost indifferent, unable or unwilling to get involved, and that in turn appeared to infect Chislenko. Quite understandably – at least if you thought Banishevsky should play – it was Edik who was left out for the second leg in Moscow a week later. We won 3-0, the best result of Yakushin's reign, and for Edik and the national team that was it. They didn't even pick him for the finals in Italy that summer – when, of course, we went out to the hosts on the toss of a coin after a 0-0 draw.

Everything was falling apart. Kuzma wasn't ever really equipped to be a head coach. People said he wasn't strong enough, and maybe that was true, but even Maslov or Morozov might have struggled wth all the crises he had to deal with, most of them to do with booze. Vladimir Shcherbakov only played one game that season and then went to CSKA because of his love of alcohol. Voronin was in decline. Edik was drinking more and more. We started to worry that he might start getting into trouble again – but he had Raisa to keep him grounded, and he was dedicated to that family.

But amid it all, there was the Cup. Edik got the winner in a fifth-round replay against CSKA. We beat UralMash Sverdlovsk 3-1 in the quarter-final, then had to go to Baku in the semis, so we all gathered round the radio in the office as usual. We won 2-0 win a goal in each half, although the game became a running battle – fists flying on the pitch, stones thrown from the stands, windows smashed on the bus as they left the stadium. Kuzma took Edik off because he was the one who seemed to draw the most violent reaction. And that was something I always pointed out when people said that Kuzma was weak: he did get rid of Shcherbakov, he was decisive then in protecting Edik. But sometimes the problems are too great no matter who is in charge.

The final, at Luzhniki, is clear in my mind – a strangely happy anti-climax. A bitter day in November, 50,000 in the Lenin Stadium, Tofiq

Bakhramov refereeing in a bobble hat, a poor game against Pakhtakor of Tashkent, and a brilliant goal. Seven minutes after half-time, a long pass from Gershkovich to Edik who, facing away from goal, backheeled it through a defender's legs to Yuri Savchenko, who poked it in. We should have had more, to be honest, but one was enough and that it came from an Edik backheel, well, in retrospect that felt appropriate. How else should an era come to an end?

Those were perhaps the last great days. We all went back to the office after, Misha and Denis and me, where Vera and Eva and the other office girls had been listening to the game. There was vodka and beer and bread and sausage and cucumbers and a celebration cake that Eva had made in secret because Misha hadn't wanted to tempt fate. I remember sitting there, late in the evening, in the warm, looking out through the window at the snow, heavy with booze and thinking how happy I was. But we never see the end till it is passed.

Глава седьмая

1969

──────── **TORPEDO** ────────

Soviet League first stage: *P18 W5 D8 L5 F15 A14 Pts18. Qualified 4th of 10.*
Soviet League second stage: *P26 W11 D9 L6 F29 A19 Pts31.* **Final position:** *5th of 14.*
Soviet Cup: *Lost in quarter-final to Sudostroitel Nikolaev.*

So Edik, and the end. The truth is nothing was ever quite as good again after that Cup final in 68. The cracks had been obvious for a while but the collapse was rapid. Anzor Kavazashvili, our Georgian keeper, had some issue with Kuzma and left for Spartak, where he won the league in 1969 and became the national first choice for the World Cup in Mexico. Valery Voronin retired. Shcherbakov lasted only a year at CSKA before winding up at Politotdel in Uzbekistan. He often came to Moscow after that with stories of what they got up to in Tashkent. Players were well-paid and discipline was lax. They would tie bags of money to a donkey and send it with a boy to a booze shop to collect their vodka. They never seemed to do anything other than drink. Shcherbakov knew his meaningful career was over but, at least as he told it, he didn't much care because he was having fun.

Edik was never somebody to abandon a friend, or at least not a male one. Whenever Shcherbak was in town, he would drink with him. Kuzma had no authority over him. That simply wasn't who he was but how, anyway, could he control his old mate? Kuzma never suffered the same backlash, but they'd missed that train to Leipzig together. That was the problem all over: Kuzma was too young, too close to too many of the players, and so while there was never any open insurrection or anything like that, neither was there the appropriate respect. There was a rumour – and I have no idea if it was true, although it certainly was in keeping with what we saw – of Kuzma telling the team he would make them really run in the next training session and Edik shrugging and saying, '*You* never used to.' And probably that was only a joke, almost certainly he didn't mean to belittle Kuzma, but that was the inevitable result.

And it wasn't only Kuzma who found it hard to deal with Edik. Boris Batanov became coach of the reserve side and he hated Edik's friendship with some of his younger charges. He would treat them as a schoolmaster treats his pupils, and then Edik would wander over and speak to him like a teammate. The lines of control became very blurred and that's never good for anybody.

There was a morning in spring when Misha came into the office and took Denis and me outside. 'Edik's not turned up again,' he said as we got into a club car. There had been a time when that would have sent a chill of anxiety through me. By this stage, though, I just felt tired. Misha usually took members of the groundstaff, strong lads, but they mustn't have been available that day. Once, I'd have felt proud that I could help the club, excited even, to be out looking for a star. But I had work to do. I didn't have the time or the energy to deal with this. We pulled up by his apartment on Mashinostroitelnaya ulitsa and got the supervisor to let us in to Edik's flat – he was only too familiar with the routine.

Edik was there, which was a relief, sprawled on the sofa, face red, mouth open, snoring. I've no idea where Raisa or the family were. He was wearing a stained grey shirt and stank of sweat and booze. Misha sent me to brew some coffee and shook him awake. He moaned softly, looked briefly startled and then, recognising Misha, grinned his insolent grin. We tipped water and coffee down him, forced his shoes onto his feet – unlaced

– pulled a coat over his shoulders and then half-carried, half-dragged him out to the car. When we got him to Myachkovo, we undressed him and sat him in the sauna, his flesh loose against the wooden slats, to sweat out some of the alcohol so he was at least able to go for a light jog. The whole thing was demeaning and depressing. This wasn't an athlete any more.

There are those who'll forgive him anything, but I was running out of patience by then. He had been welcomed back, we'd fought for him to come back, and he'd betrayed that trust. That was who he was, they said. He couldn't help it. He was an unserious man disposed to drink. Just as some had always demanded more and more from his ability, so others forgave him everything for his talent. For me, though, that just made it worse. He had a responsibility to his genius and he squandered it. I know he was under pressure. I know his feet hurt. I know it was hard to play to his maximum every week. I'd defended him on those grounds myself. But there are limits. Everybody's life is hard in its own way. Mine certainly was.

Does that sound bitter? Perhaps it does. But there were times when I looked at my leg and everything that was an effort for me that other people took for granted and I looked at him, and I wondered what I might have done with his gifts. But I never said anything because, well, you didn't. He was still Edik, and he still had his charm, still had his power.

He started missing deadlines, arriving late or not turning up at all. His body, that mighty frame that had survived the camps, began to let him down. He began to look unfit. He started to suffer from piles. His metabolism slowed down and he gained weight. And his flat feet began to afflict him more and more.

They were craven. They could have taken action and they didn't. They just gossiped about him, complained about him behind his back. That had happened before, of course, although perhaps not so often, but he could silence the moaners with a goal. In 1969, there were no goals. None at all.

Not only that, but there were some terrible misses. Worst of all, of course, was the Cup quarter-final against Sudostroitel of Nikolaev when they let in two in the first half, when Gershkovich got one back and Edik had the chance to equalise only to put it miles wide. As his body failed him, so too did his technique.

Edik moved back into midfield, that age-old get out for a striker losing his sharpness. Let him drop deep, they'd say, let him spray it about a bit. But that almost never worked. Football is harder than that. He was left out of some games, playing in the reserves to get his fitness and confidence back. They started to say Vadim Nikonov was being prepared to be Edik's successor, although he was a player much more similar in style to Kuzma. But then maybe that was the point, to flatter the coach and encourage him to nudge Edik aside. There were politics everywhere in those days.

....

It was a stifling hot Sunday afternoon in August. We didn't often go to watch the reserves in those days but Edik was playing and Eva had taken the kids to visit her parents in Yaroslavl so Misha had a free day. Looking back at the records, I see we were 2-1 up at half-time, but I don't remember that. I don't remember either goal. What I remember is what happened in the second half.

A ball was played in to Edik with his back to goal. It bounced up slightly and as he moved to control it the Dinamo Moscow hardman Sergei Nikulin caught his standing leg from behind. It was obvious straightaway the injury was serious – something about the noise of boot on leg, the way Edik fell, his shout of pain. I remember glancing at Misha and seeing his eyes closed, face angled down. And then he snapped into work mode and went to supervise Edik's transport to the Central Institute of Traumatology and Orthopaedics.

First impressions were confirmed: a ruptured Achilles tendon. You can say you couldn't blame his lifestyle for that, but then if it hadn't been for his lifestyle, he wouldn't have been playing for the reserves. Maybe his movement would have been quicker. Maybe the tendon would have been better able to absorb the impact. That night, we later discovered, Igor Chislenko went to visit Edik and hid a crate of brandy under the bed.

It was a stupid way for it all to end. Edik came back the following April, coming off the bench in Tashkent, but he still wasn't ready. He returned about a month later and managed six games in a row, but it wasn't Edik. He was done. His last game came at home to Dinamo Minsk that September. It had been against them he'd scored his first goal after prison, his first in seven years; this time the drought was only two years, but it turned out to be forever. The great goalscorer ended his career with a run of 23 games without a goal.

Perhaps from the outside we read too much into small details. Perhaps we project our own feelings onto our heroes. But it seemed to me that Edik by then barely cared. He knew it was over just as surely as everybody else did. He had fought to survive in the camps, and he had fought to return to fitness and play after his release, but by then, at 33, the fight had left him.

He stopped going to Myachkovo, and nobody came to collect him. He spoke to Kuzma on the telephone and asked if he should come to training. 'If you want to,' Kuzma replied. He didn't bother.

We later heard from somebody – Vera, maybe? I can't recall – that a few months earlier he'd told Raisa he was playing on only as long as it took for ZIL to give him a fridge. Did he get his fridge? I never found out. But abruptly, with no ceremony, no send-off, no emotional farewells, it was over. Edik retired. Some fans of my generation fell almost into a second mourning for him. Even Misha, I think, although there was an element of relief that he wasn't constantly having to monitor his behaviour, felt some sense of bereavement. And me? It was like when an ageing relative who has been sick for years finally passes. You cannot be shocked and you cannot rail against the universe, but the moment of passing makes you realise what has been lost. And for me that was not only a great talent but something more profound. It was only in those final years I realised how much I had invested in Edik and how ill-equipped he had been to carry my dreams and those of the factory and beyond.

....

Edik had good intentions. He wanted to get the qualifications to become a coach. He went to classes and was given a stipend by ZIL. Gershkovich would go to his flat to study with him. He said that Edik was smart, that he picked up ideas quickly, but also that he struggled to concentrate for long periods, that he kept going off to the kitchen to refresh himself with a shot of vodka. Raisa took to hiding the wine and Edik would call on her at work to beg her to tell him where she'd put it.

He got his badges. He became a coach. He worked with the kids at Torpedo. But I think he was bored. You'd see him around the place and at first it felt good to have him there, a reminder of the club's greatness.There had been a time when I'd felt a thrill every time I saw him off the pitch. But after a while, I began to try to avoid him. Maybe that was cowardly on my part, but it was an awful thing to see, an athlete like that, a demigod, become this balding red-faced middle-aged man who needed glasses and was often hungover. And I worried always I might let slip how I'd come to feel about him, that I felt betrayed by him.

It happens. Of course it happens. Age attacks sportsmen harder than others. For 10 or 12 or maybe 15 years, they are stronger, quicker and more powerful than other men, they are adored and they live for that adrenaline rush of a goal being scored or a game being won. Of course, for them, all subsequent life is anti-climax. The rest of us can still dream, almost until death has claimed us, of a promotion, or watching our team win the league, or love. But for those who have been there, who have done great things, who have promoted and deserved the applause, what is left when their bodies begin to fail them? A few, perhaps, become great coaches. For others, the satisfaction of a family is enough – and Edik, it should be said, seemed happy with Raisa, devoted to her children in a way he never was to Mila. But he always seemed diminished. I couldn't help but see him in middle age and think of the boy he had been, the power he had had, the joy with which he hit those shots at ridiculous velocity.

Eva never aged.

She was killed in October 1970, a month after Edik's final game, still beautiful, still gentle, still wise, hit by a truck on the corner of Masterkova and Leninskaya Sloboda, dead before she reached the hospital. The driver had been drunk.

Misha never truly recovered. Briefly he gave up vodka but after a few months took to it as though making up for lost time. He settled down eventually, but there was always a sadness about him after that. It may be that times had moved on, that the committees and back channels he had negotiated so skilfully had changed, but his career stalled. He became just another weary man in the office who drank too much, a few rungs above me, but no longer the high flyer he had been.

It affected me as well, her death. Not as much as it hit poor Misha, of course, or the kids, but she was special to me as well. Being in her company, listening to her ideas, gave me a warm glow inside. She left a huge vacuum in the lives of all of us who had known her. I suppose in my own slightly distant way I loved her. She offered a sense of something better and then she was gone.

For a while, she flickered still at the edge of my consciousness. There were times when I thought I glimpsed her, turning a corner in the offices, leaving the canteen, when I forgot. We got by, I suppose, Misha and me, watching football, discussing football, remembering football. It gave us something to do and it had been part of our lives for so long that it gave us an essential structure.

We weren't at the World Cup in 74 – expelled after refusing to play a play-off in a stadium in Santiago that had doubled as a death camp for Pinochet – or in 1978, eliminated after a stupid defeat in Greece, but I remember watching the World Cup from Spain in 82 in the office, just like we'd used to do, and having a sense that everything might work out, that things hadn't changed so much. Vera was retired by then, but there was me and Misha, sometimes Denis, and a couple of young lads who tolerated our ancient grumbling in exchange for vodka.

That was a lovely side, under Beskov, with the three great Georgians. The defeat to Brazil was one of the best games I've ever seen, then there was the tension of the draw against Scotland, with Ramaz Shengelia's late goal and Graeme Souness's even later equaliser. And then the frustration of the draw against Poland in the second phase when we needed a win to make the semi-final, when Vitaly Daraselia, who had scored the late winner for Dinamo Tbilisi in the Cup Winners' Cup final the year before, was thrown on far too late. But there was no cake and no Eva, and I couldn't help but feel the absence. Then Daraselia was also dead within six months, driving his car off a cliff into a river. It had only been a few months earlier that Nikolai Morozov had died, killed, the rumour said, in a bar brawl near Lokomotiv's ground – something to do with his new girlfriend. But if you leave your wife when you're 60... I'm rambling, but this is what happens with memory.

Death seemed everywhere in those days. And of course it is. If you live long enough the list of those you have known who have gone soon adds up. Edik joined it in 1990, chewed up by cancer. As Misha said, and I'm sure the thought was provoked by his feelings about his own life after Eva had been killed, it was his second death: the first had come when he had retired from football and the long slow journey to the grave had begun. I didn't say it but I would argue it was his third: the dream of Edik had died in that dacha in May 1958.

It's very easy to forgive weakness in a man, very easy to joke about the childish grin on a face flushed with booze, but there are consequences. That night at the dacha a young woman was punched in the eye and raped. Naivety or a love of alcohol cannot excuse that. He was careless and that damaged others as well as himself. Who thinks now of Alla or Mila? Or even Marina?

They still met up for a time, Alla and Edik. He made the usual promises about making financial contributions that he could never keep. I doubt Alla believed him any more. Then she moved out to Chertanovo and I think with the travel she just couldn't be bothered to make the effort to see him any more. With his new family it was completely different. So maybe you could say he had learned, but that didn't help Alla or Mila. The sadness is how much he seemed by then to need a family.

As time went by, as Andropov gave way to Chernenko and then Gorbachev, what we now know to have been cancer ate away at him. I saw him round the club less and less. His hair grew even thinner, lost its blond sheen. His face became thinner. Greyness replaced the red. Age, we thought: it erases us all. Some of us lose our hair, some of us stoop, some of us struggle to sleep. It made him smaller. Cancer made our hero mortal in a way the years in the camps had not. Those who knew him said he remained good company. By then I didn't want to know.

I wanted to remember him as he had been, to remember the thrill he had provoked deep within me when he first scored in Tbilisi, when he brushed defenders aside and battered the ball past goalkeepers seemingly every week, when he transformed that Olympic semi-final against Bulgaria, before the drink took him, before the dacha. You couldn't see him shuffling along a corridor in those later years and not feel pity. But pity is not forgiveness.

Edik offered us a vision of something great and beautiful and that invested him with a responsibility he never sought or seemed capable of bearing. He failed to sustain it. Perhaps that was inevitable. We all age. But others might have handled that better, might not have hastened their own destruction. Others might have failed differently, might have failed better.

And others would not have done what he did to Marina. I thought of her often after I saw her that morning at Vagankovo – if it had been her. What had happened to her after the trial? Where had she gone? What did she feel when he came back, when we won the league, when he played again for the country? Maybe she wanted to be forgotten, but we had forgotten her.

I left her rose alone on the grave, poignantly red against the grey earth. But I knew it too would fade with time.

Eduard Anatolyevich Streltsov
21 July 1937 – 22 July 1990

SENIOR CAREER*			
Years	Team	Apps	Goals
1953–1958	Torpedo Moscow	89	48
1965–1970	Torpedo Moscow	133	51
NATIONAL TEAM			
1955–1968	Soviet Union	38	25

Senior club appearances and goals counted for the domestic league only